Pocket Guide
To Depression
Glass

Revised Second Edition

By Gene Florence

COLLECTOR BOOKS
P.O. Box 3009
Paducah, Kentucky 42001

The current values in this book should be used only as a guide. They are not intended to set prices, which vary from one section of the country to another. Auction prices as well as dealer prices vary greatly and are affected by condition as well as demand. Neither the Author nor the Publisher assumes responsibility for any losses that might be incurred as a result of consulting this guide.

Additional copies of this book may be ordered from:

COLLECTOR BOOKS
P.O. Box 3009
Paducah, Kentucky 42001
or
Gene Florence
P.O. Box 22186
Lexington, Kentucky 40522

@$8.95 Add $1.00 for postage and handling.

Printed by IMAGE GRAPHICS, Paducah, Kentucky

FOREWORD

Depression Glass as defined in this book is the colored glassware made primarily during the Depression years in the colors of amber, green, pink, blue, red, yellow, white and crystal. There are other colors and some of the glassware included in this book was made later than the Depression era; but it has still been collected as that era glassware because of its color. The main emphasis of this book is given to the inexpensively made glassware produced in quantity and sold through the five and dime stores or given away as premiums or included with the purchase of other products, i.e. the spice shaker contained a certain brand spice.

Information for this book has come from over 300,000 miles of travel throughout the country in connection with glassware over the past seven years and from the research and sale of over 150,000 copies of the Collector's Encyclopedia of Depression Glass.

ACKNOWLEDGEMENTS

I would like at this time to say a word of thanks to the people who generously lent their glassware to be photographed. They are as follows: John and Trannie Davis, Helen Marshall, Lois Florence, my sister, and my mother, Gladys Florence of Grannie Bear Antiques.

Also, a special thanks to my family for their support in various ways, gathering bits of information, taking over my responsibilities to leave me free to write. Again my wife, Cathy, struggled with my handwriting to serve as typist and editor for this little book. Anyone having seen my handwriting will realize this was no small task.

A special thanks to Dana Curtis, Curtis and Mays Photographic Studio & Gallery of Paducah, Kentucky for the photographs in the book.

CONTENTS

PRICING

Glass that is in less than mint condition, i.e. chipped, cracked, scratched or poorly molded, will bring very small prices unless extremely rare; and then, will bring only a small percentage of the price of glass that is in mint condition.

This book is meant as a guide to price; however, if your Depression Glass comes to you at bargain rates or free from a relative, then that's all to the good!

Prices have become almost standardized due to national advertising by dealers and due to the Depression Glass Shows which are held from coast to coast. However, there are some regional differences in prices due to glass being more readily available in some areas of the country than in others. Too, companies distributed certain pieces in some areas that it did not in others.

NOTICE

A listing of the colors to be found in each pattern is mentioned under the photo headings. However, the prices catalogued herein represent those colors most commonly collected in each pattern. See THE COLLECTOR'S ENCYCLOPEDIA OF DEPRRESSION GLASS should you desire more detailed information.

HOW TO FIND DEPRESSION GLASS

The best place to find Depression Glass is in your own basement, garage or attic—or even in your own cupboards. Yes, that's true. Nearly everyone has at least a piece or two around their own home; it may be a bowl that belonged to grandmother and got handed down; it may be a complete setting that an aunt or someone got as a wedding gift and packed away for storage in the attic.

First of all, you need to learn to recognize the colors Depression Glass comes in for often the coloring of the glass is recognizable as Depression era glassware even when the pattern name is yet unknown. That was primarily the reason for making this book a full color book so that the novice collector could acquaint himself with the full range of colors the glass may be found in.

Once you have searched your own shelves and those of your immediate relatives and friends, your next source for finding Depression Glass should be the garage sales, tag sales, yard sales, etc. where people are cleaning out their attics and garages. Don't forget the church bazaar, the Salvation Army store or the Volunteers of America. You'll find competition is keen at these latter places; so you'll need to shop early.

Now that you've covered all the afore mentioned places, it's time to make a tour of the antique and junk shops in your area. These are often gold mines of the ridiculous to the sublime price wise; so have in mind what you'll pay for a particular item. Too, most of these shops expect to haggle a bit over price; so don't be shy.

Household and estate auctions are often another valuable source for finding Depression Glass; but it is wise to check out the merchandise before making a bid as chips and small damage to an item may be overlooked by the harried auctioneer.

Many collectors feel that antique shows and flea markets are the very best places to find Depression Glass. So, don't forget to put these on your agenda. Under the heading FLEA MARKETS, I shall list some of the bigger ones that are held around the country.

I find my best sources for finding the particular pieces and patterns in Depression Glass are the Depression Glass Shows put on by clubs throughout the country and the publications which deal primarily in Depression era glass. You will find two of the best listed on page 159 of this book. There are other publications, of course; but for overall information and volume of advertisement of glass, I like these two.

DEPRESSION GLASS CLUBS

It would be impractical to list the numerous clubs and their addresses here as there are over 200 active clubs to date and the number is rapidly expanding. However, the publications listed on page 159 of this book carry a listing with addresses for corresponding with these clubs. Most clubs meet monthly and many of them are good places to learn about the glass itself. In all you'll find someone to share your enthusiasm and help you in your quest for glass.

DEPRESSION GLASS SHOWS

You can't describe the face of a first time visitor to a Depression Glass Show. Just imagine walking into a room with 20,000 to 50,000 pieces of Depression Glass artistically displayed in booths throughout the room. It boggles the mind; and it's an event you'll want to see again and again. It would be impossible to mention all the shows that are put on in a year's time, but below is a partial listing of a few of the bigger shows put on regularly throughout the country. (The asterisk indicates that the shows are club sponsored).

January	San Jose, Calif.
	Sanford, Fla. (last weekend)
February	*Sacramento, Calif.
	*Miami, Fla. (1st weekend)
	*New Orleans, La.
	*Houston, Tx. (last weekend)
March	Charlotte, N.C.
March/April	*Greenbelt, Md.
	*Southington, Conn.
April	*Denver, Colo.
	*Pittsburg, Pa.
	*Springfield, Ill.
	*St. Louis, Mo.
May	*Rochester, Mich.
	Anaheim, Calif.
June	San Jose, Calif. (1st weekend)
July	*Marietta, Ga. (Civic Center - 4th weekend)

August	Pensacola, Fla.
	*Sacramento, Calif.
September	*New Orleans, La.
	*Lakeland, Fla.
October	Marietta, Ga. (Civic Center - 1st weekend)
	*Cleveland, Ohio
	*Ypsilanti, Mich. (3rd weekend)
	*Milwaukee, Wisc.
November	*Cincinnati, Ohio (1st weekend)
	Anaheim, Calif.
	*St. Louis, Mo.

Several promoters of Depression Glass shows can be written to for their calendar of shows put on throughout the year across the country:

DOGWOOD PRODUCTIONS
4964 Bartow St. N.W.
Acworth, Ga. 30101

CAMEO PRODUCTION
Box 2315F
Costa Mesa, Calif. 92626

J&B PROMOTION
1125F E. Princeton Ave.
Ontario, Calif. 91764

HEAVENLY PRODUCTIONS
582 Carpentier Way
San Jose, Calif. 95111

SELLING

One of the purposes of this book is to help you make money from any of your unwanted glassware treasures; any number of books infer that there are treasures in your attic, but few tell you how to reap benefits from them. To find a reputable dealer in your area is not always an easy task; but here are a few suggestions. If you live in an area where a show is held regularly, watch for advertisements and attend the show. You might find a buyer for your glass among the dealers at the show. If there is a Depression Glass Club meeting in your area, there may be members there who would be willing to buy your glass or who could put you in contact with someone who would. Failing either of those methods, you could send for a sample copy of one of the publications listed at the end of the book and seek a dealer in your area by looking through the ads. The telephone directory or the ads under antiques in your local newspaper may lead you to a dealer in glass who would be interested in buying yours; or you might take it to a local flea market and find a buyer among the dealers set up there.

The prices herein are retail and you can expect to receive 60 to 70% of the prices listed for the popular, highly collectible patterns, but only 40 to 50% of prices listed for the patterns that are not as avidly sought by collectors.

There are several factors a dealer will consider when offering for your piece: it's condition, how popular this color is with potential buyers, whether or not the pattern is one numerous people collect, whether he has plenty in stock already, whether he thinks he can make money on the piece before he's had to pack it up at 65 different shows throughout the country or dropped it and broken it. Popularity of a pattern and the demand for it are the two key factors in interesting a potention buyer of your glassware. This book should give you an accurate guide as to what to expect for your glass. You shouldn't be walking up to a dealer without the faintest idea of what your glass is worth; neither should you expect him to pay you retail price for the glass if you're sincerely wanting him to buy it.

FLEA MARKETS

Flea Markets can be found in almost every state which are open on a regular basis either weekly, monthly or bi-monthly. I am listing herein a few of the better known, larger and more widely advertised ones that I have attended personally. Pay particlular attention to the advertisements in the classified section of your newspaper around big holidays such as Memorial Day, 4th of July and Labor Day as many of the bigger flea markets congregate on these dates.

California — Pasadena, monthly at the Rosebowl

Indiana — Indianapolis, particularly at the fairgrounds

Kentucky — Louisville, regular shows at the fairgrounds

Massachusetts — Brimfield, shows in May, July, September

Ohio — Hartville, every Monday
Manesfield, monthly
Springfield, monthly
Washington Court House,
   monthly except July at Fairgrounds

Pennsylvania — Lancaster/Reading Area—many weekly

Texas — Canton, weekend of 1st Monday in month

These represent but a drop in the bucket of all the flea markets that one can find in the cities around the country; they are advertised both in the local newspapers and in the various trade publications, a couple of which are listed in the back of this book.

WHAT TO COLLECT—HELPFUL HINT SECTION

Many beginning collectors make the mistake of trying to collect everything in sight; and unless you have a few oil wells on the side, you can soon find yourself out of funds doing this.

My first suggestion is to study this book. Most of you have looked at the pictures before even starting to read this; that's a start. You have a general idea of what's available. Decide on one or possibly two patterns you like; once you see it close at hand, you may change your mind; but that's all right. Collectors do that for a variety of reasons. However, it's wise to settle on something specific to look for rather than to pick and choose at random.

If money is a problem, peruse the prices of the various patterns and choose one that is less expensive to collect. However, you should become familiar with the whole range of patterns and you should have a general idea of the range of price on the more expensive pieces of the patterns because everyone, sooner or later, stumbles onto a piece of glass worth $50 that's priced at $5.00; and even if you don't care for the piece or the pattern, you should go ahead and buy it because you'll either be able to trade it to someone who does want it for the pattern you want, or you can sell it and use the extra money to buy the glass you like.

In the early 1960's through the early 1970's, you could buy depression glass by the box and crate loads at auctions for a song; thus, you could afford to collect several patterns at once; however, those days have come to an end; so, it's better to have something definite in mind to collect.

If money is no problem, then by all means, choose one of the more expensive patterns to collect; as there are more people wanting these patterns usually, the market value of your pattern will be stable at the least, and will probably increase as the years pass.

Some people don't choose to collect an entire pattern; they collect one piece of every pattern, say plates; one California collector collects only cookie jars; another I know collects only candy jars; there are numerous salt and pepper collections; so you could choose to collect only one or two pieces of several patterns. In any case, you'll find the glass attractive to serve in and a real item of conversation.

If you are hard bitten by the bug of collecting Depression Glass, then you might possibly want a more detailed guide for the glass; should that happen, I'd be delighted to recommend my Collector's Encyclopedia of Depression Glass, which can be ordered from this publisher or myself. I receive letters daily from its delighted readers. In any case, happy hunting—and even happier finding. It's a hobby I think you'll not only enjoy but one from which you'll profit.

ADAM (pink, green)

JEANNETTE GLASS COMPANY 1932-1934

	Pink/Green
Ash Tray, 4½"	16.00/14.00
Bowl, 4¾" Dessert	6.50/7.00
Bowl, 5¾" Cereal	16.00/13.00
Bowl, 7¾"	9.50/12.00
Bowl, 9" Covered	27.50/50.00
Bowl, 10" Oval	12.00/15.00
Butter Dish & Cover	60.00/195.00
Cake Plate, 10" Footed	9.00/14.00
Candlesticks, 4" Pair	37.50/55.00
Candy Jar & Cover, 2½"	40.00/50.00
Coaster, 3¾"	13.00/9.50
Creamer	8.00/9.00
Cup	13.00/12.50
Lamp	75.00/75.00
Pitcher, 8", 32 oz	20.00/25.00

	Pink/Green
Plate, 6" Sherbet	3.00/3.00
Plate, 7¾" Sq. Salad	6.00/6.25
Plate, 9" Sq. Dinner	10.50/11.00
Plate, 9" Grill	9.00/8.00
Platter, 11 ¾"	8.50/10.00
Relish Dish, 8" Divided	6.00/8.00
Salt & Pepper, 4"	35.00/65.00
Saucer, Sq. 6"	2.50/2.50
Sherbet, 3"	9.50/13.50
Sugar	7.50/9.75
Sugar/Candy cover	11.00/15.00
Tumbler, 4½"	11.50/11.50
Tumbler, 5½" Iced Tea	25.00/21.00
Vase, 7½"	90.00/25.00

16

AMERICAN PIONEER
(pink, green, amber, crystal)
LIBERTY WORKS 1931-1934

	Pink/Green
Bowl, 5" handled	7.00/8.00
Bowl, 8¾" covered	50.00/60.00
Bowl, 9" handled	9.00/12.00
Bowl, console 10-3/8"	30.00/40.00
Candlesticks, 6½" pair	40.00/50.00
Candy Jar and Cover, 1 lb.	30.00/40.00
Candy Jar and Cover, 1½ lb.	40.00/55.00
Cheese and Cracker Set (indented platter & compote)	15.00/17.50
Coaster, 3½"	10.00/12.00
Creamer, 2¾"	5.50/6.50
Creamer, 3½"	6.00/7.00
Cup	4.00/6.00
Dresser Set (2 cologne, powder jar, on indented 7½" tray)	75.00/90.00

	Pink/Green
Goblet, Wine, 4", 3 oz.	12.00/15.00
Goblet, Water, 6", 8 oz.	15.00/18.00
Ice Bucket, 6"	17.50/25.00
Lamp, 8½" tall	50.00/65.00
Pitcher, 5" covered urn	75.00/100.00
Pitcher, 7" covered urn	95.00/125.00
Plate, 8"	4.25/3.75
Plate, 11½" handled	8.00/10.50
Saucer	2.00/2.00
Sugar, 2¾"	4.00/5.00
Sugar, 3½"	5.00/6.00
Tumbler, 4", 8 oz.	12.00/15.00
Tumbler, 5", 12 oz.	15.00/25.00
Vase, rose bowl, 16 oz. 4¼", ftd.	35.00/50.00
Vase, 7", three styles, rolled, or crimped edge, straight	50.00/65.00

AMERICAN SWEETHEART
(pink, monax, cremax, red and blue)
MACBETH EVANS GLASS COMPANY 1930-1936

	Pink/Monax
Bowl, 3¾" Flat, Berry ...	16.00/-----
Bowl, 4½", Cream Soup .	17.00/32.50
Bowl, 6" Cereal.........	6.50/8.50
Bowl, 9" Round, Berry ...	12.50/30.00
Bowl, 9½" Flat Soup	16.50/32.00
Bowl, 11" Oval Vegetable	20.00/35.00
Creamer, Footed	5.50/6.50
Cup.................	8.00/7.25
Plate, 6"	
Bread and Butter	2.50/3.25
Plate, 8" Salad	4.50/6.00
Plate, 9" Luncheon	-----/6.50
Plate 9¾" - 10¼" Dinner	12.00/12.50

	Pink/Monax
Plate, 12" Salver........	8.00/11.00
Platter, 13" Oval........	13.50/32.50
Pitcher, 7½", 60 oz......	250.00/-----
Pitcher, 8", 80 oz........	225.00/-----
Salt and Pepper, Footed .	200.00/195.00
Saucer	2.50/2.25
Sherbet, Footed, 4"	9.50/-----
Sherbet, Footed, 4¼" ...	7.00/13.00
Sugar, Open, Footed	5.50/5.75
Sugar Cover	-----/135.00
Tumbler, 3½", 5 oz......	22.00/-----
Tumbler, 4", 9 oz........	20.00/-----
Tumbler, 4½", 10 oz.....	23.50/-----

ANNIVERSARY
(pink) (recently in crystal and iridescent)
JEANNETTE GLASS COMPANY 1947-1949

	Crystal/Pink		Crystal/Pink
Bowl, 4-7/8" Berry	1.00/2.00	Plate, 6¼" Sherbet	.75/1.75
Bowl, 7-3/8" Soup	3.00/5.00	Plate, 9" Dinner	2.50/4.00
Bowl, 9" Fruit	7.00/10.00	Plate, 12½"	
Butter Dish and Cover	22.00/37.50	Sandwich Server	4.00/6.00
Candy Jar and Cover	15.00/20.00	Relish Dish, 8"	4.00/6.00
Compote, Open, 3		Saucer	1.00/1.50
Legged	3.00/6.00	Sherbet, Footed	2.00/3.75
Cake Plate, 12½"	5.00/8.00	Sugar	2.00/4.00
Cake Plate with Cover	10.00/12.00	Sugar Cover	2.50/4.00
Creamer, Footed	3.00/5.75	Vase, 6½"	5.00/8.00
Cup	2.00/3.50	Vase, Wall Pin-up	9.00/12.00
Pickle Dish, 9"	3.00/5.00	Wine Glass, 2½ oz.	4.00/7.00

AUNT POLLY
(green, blue, iridescent)
U.S. GLASS COMPANY Late 1920's

	Green/Blue
Bowl, 4-3/8" Berry	3.00/4.00
Bowl, 4¾" 2" High	8.00/10.00
Bowl, 7¼" Oval, Handled Pickle	8.00/10.00
Bowl, 7-7/8" Large Berry	10.00/12.50
Bowl, 8-3/8" Oval	15.00/20.00
Butter Dish and Cover	125.00/100.00
Candy, Cover, Two Handled	20.00/30.00

	Green/Blue
Creamer	15.00/18.00
Pitcher, 8", 48 oz.	-----/90.00
Plate, 6" Sherbet	2.50/3.00
Plate, 8" Luncheon	5.00/6.00
Salt and Pepper	-----/125.00
Sherbet	7.50/6.50
Sugar	10.00/12.00
Sugar Cover	25.00/35.00
Tumbler, 3-5/8", 8 oz.	-----/11.00
Vase, 6½", Footed	20.00/22.00

AVOCADO, "SWEET PEAR", No. 601
(pink, green)
INDIANA GLASS COMPANY 1923-1933

	Pink/Green		Pink/Green
Bowl, 5¼", Two-Handled	15.00/17.50	Cup, Footed	22.00/25.00
Bowl, 6" Relish, Footed ..	13.00/17.50	Pitcher, 64 ozs.	300.00/450.00
Bowl, 7" Preserve		Plate, 6¼" Sherbet	6.00/8.00
One Handle	11.00/13.50	Plate, 8¼" Luncheon	9.50/12.50
Bowl, 7½" Salad	22.00/30.00	Plate, 10¼"	
Bowl, 8" Oval,		Two Handled Cake	20.00/29.00
Two-Handled	13.00/17.00	Saucer	15.00/20.00
Bowl, 8½" Berry	25.00/30.00	Sherbet	40.00/47.50
Bowl, 9½", 3¼" Deep	40.00/60.00	Sugar, Footed	18.00/25.00
Creamer, Footed	22.00/27.00	Tumbler	45.00/95.00

BEADED BLOCK
(pink, green, crystal, ice blue, vaseline, iridescent, amber, opalescent colors)
IMPERIAL GLASS COMPANY 1927-1930's

	Pink/Opalescent
Bowl, 4½"	
2 handled jelly	5.00/11.00
Bowl, 4½", round, lily . . .	8.00/13.50
Bowl, 5½", square	5.00/6.50
Bowl, 5½", 1 handle	6.00/8.00
Bowl, 6", deep, round . . .	8.00/12.00
Bowl, 6¼", round	6.00/12.00
Bowl, 6½', round	6.00/12.50
Bowl, 6½',	
2 handled pickle	9.50/13.50
Bowl, 6¾"	
round, unflared	8.25/11.00
Bowl, 7¼", round, flared	7.50/13.50

	Pink/Opalescent
Bowl, 7½", round,	
fluted edges	16.50/17.50
Bowl, 7½", round,	
plain edge	7.00/12.00
Bowl, 8¼", celery	8.50/12.50
Creamer	8.50/15.00
Pitcher, 5¼", Pint Jug . . .	97.50/-----
Plate, 7¾" Sq.	4.50/7.25
Plate, 8¾", round	5.00/9.50
Stemmed Jelly, 4½"	6.50/12.50
Stemmed Jelly,	
4½", flared top	8.00/15.00
Sugar	8.50/15.00
Vase, 6", bouquet	7.50/15.00

BLOCK OPTIC, "BLOCK"
(green, pink, yellow, crystal)
HOCKING GLASS COMPANY 1929-1933

	Pink/Green		Pink/Green
Bowl, 4¼", Berry	3.50/3.75	Mug, Flat Creamer	
Bowl, 5¼", Cereal	4.50/5.75	No Spout	15.00/20.00
Bowl, 7", Salad	7.50/10.00	Pitcher, 8½, 54 oz.	20.00/25.00
Bowl, 8½", Large Berry	9.00/9.50	Pitcher, 8", 80 oz.	20.00/27.50
Butter Dish & Cover		Plate, 6" Sherbet	1.35/1.50
3" x 5"	20.00/22.50	Plate, 8" Luncheon	2.00/2.25
Candlestick, 1¾", Pr.	20.00/21.50	Plate, 9" Dinner	7.00/8.50
Candy Jar and Cover,		Plate, 9" Grill	5.00/7.00
2¼"	19.00/17.50	Salt and Pepper, Footed	15.00/18.00
Candy Jar Cover, 6¼"	25.00/27.50	Salt and Pepper, Squatty	20.00/20.00
Compote, 4" Wide		Sandwich Server,	
Mayonnaise	10.00/12.00	Center Handle	-----/25.00
Creamer, Three Styles:		Saucer	3.50/3.50
Cone Shaped, Round,		Sherbet, Non Stemmed	4.00/2.75
Footed & Flat	4.00/4.50	Sherbet, 3¼", 5½ oz.	3.75/3.00
Cup, Four Styles	2.50/3.00	Sherbet, 4¾", 6 oz.	7.00/9.00
Goblet, 4", Cocktail	9.00/12.00	Sugar, Three Styles:	
Goblet, 4½", Wine	10.00/12.50	As Creamer	3.00/4.50
Goblet, 5¾", 9 oz.	8.50/10.00	Tumbler, 3½", 5 oz. Flat	4.00/8.00
Goblet, 7¼", Thin, 9 oz.	12.50/15.00	Tumbler, 4", 5 oz. Flooted	5.00/9.00
Ice Tub or Butter Tub		Tumbler, 9 oz. Flat	8.00/5.00
Open	15.00/16.00	Tumbler, 9 oz. Footed	8.50/11.50

	Pink/Green		Pink/Green
Tumbler, 10 oz. Flat	7.00/8.00	Tumble-up Night Set:	
Tumbler, 6",		3" Tumbler Bottle and	
10 oz. Footed	7.50/12.00	Tumbler, 6" High	30.00/35.00
		Vase, 5¾, Blown	-----/100.00
		Whiskey, 2½"	6.50/10.00

"BOWKNOT"
(green)
UNKNOWN MANUFACTURER

	Green		Green
Bowl, 4½", Berry	7.00	Sherbet, Low Footed	6.50
Bowl, 5½", Cereal	9.00	Tumbler, 5", 10 oz.......	8.50
Cup.................	5.50	Tumbler, 5", 10 oz.	
Plate, 7", Salad	5.00	Footed	7.00

"BUBBLE", "FIRE KING"
(blue, dark green, ruby red, crystal)
HOCKING GLASS COMPANY 1934-1965

	Crystal/Blue
Bowl, 4", Berry	2.00/6.00
Bowl, 4½", Fruit	2.00/4.00
Bowl, 5¼", Cereal	2.00/4.50
Bowl, 7¾", Flat Soup	4.00/5.50
Bowl, 8 3/8, Large Berry	3.00/6.00
Creamer	2.50/15.00
Cup	2.00/2.50
Pitcher, 64 oz., Ice Lip (Red)	30.00
Plate, 6¾" Bread & Butter	.50/1.00
Plate, 9 3/8", Grill	-----/5.00

	Crystal/Blue
Plate 9 3/8", Dinner	2.00/3.50
Platter, 12", Oval	3.00/5.50
Saucer	.50/1.35
Sugar	2.50/8.00
Tumbler, 6 oz., Juice (Red)	-----/5.00
Tumbler, 9 oz. Water (Red)	-----/4.50
Tumbler, 12 oz. Iced Tea (Red)	-----/8.00
Tumbler, 16 oz., Lemonade (Red)	-----/10.00

26

CAMEO, "BALLERINA," or "DANCING GIRL"
(green, yellow, pink and crystal with a platinum rim)
HOCKING GLASS COMPANY 1930-1934

	Green/Yellow		Green/Yellow
Bowl, 4¾" Cream Soup ..	40.00/-----	Cup, Two Styles	9.00/5.00
Bowl, 5½" Cereal.......	10.00/12.00	Decanter, 10",	
Bowl, 7¼", Salad	20.00/-----	W/Stopper...........	55.00/-----
Bowl, 8¼", Large Berry ..	20.00/-----	Decanter, 10"	
Bowl, 9", Rimmed Soup ..	22.00/-----	W/Stopper, Frosted	
Bowl, 10", Oval		(Stoppers Represent ½	
Vegetable	9.00/15.00	Value of Decanter)....	20.00/-----
Bowl, 11", 3 Leg Console .	30.00/45.00	Domino Tray, 7" With 3"	
Butter Dish & Cover	120.00/600.00	Identation	50.00/-----
Cake Plate, 10", 3 Legs ..	11.00/-----	Goblet, 3½", Wine	90.00/-----
Candlesticks, 4" Pr.	55.00/-----	Goblet, 4", Wine	40.00/-----
Candy Jar, Low 4"		Goblet, 6", Water.......	27.50/-----
Cover	35.00/40.00	Ice Bowl or Open Butter	
Candy Jar, 6½" Tall		3" Tall x 5½" Wide	85.00/-----
& Cover	77.50/-----	Jam Jar, 2" and Cover ...	67.50/-----
Cocktail Shaker (Metal		Pitcher, 5¾", Syrup or	
Lid) Appears in Crystal		Milk, 20 oz.	120.00/250.00
Only	-----/150.00	Pitcher, 6" Juice, 36 oz.. .	32.50/-----
Compote, 4" Wide,		Pitcher, 8½", Water,	
Mayonnaise	15.00/-----	56 oz.	30.00/-----
Cookie Jar & Cover	25.00/-----	Plate, 6" Sherbet	2.50/1.75
Creamer, 3¼"	12.50/11.50	Plate, 8", Luncheon	4.50/4.00
Creamer, 4¼"	13.50/-----	Plate, 8½" Square	18.00/50.00

	Green/Yellow
Plate, 9½, Dinner	9.50/5.50
Plate, 10", Sandwich	7.50/-----
Plate, 10½", Grill.......	6.50/6.00
Plate, 10½", Grill With	
Closed Handles.......	6.50/5.00
Plate, 11½", With	
Closed Handles.......	6.00/5.00
Platter, 12",	
Closed Handles.......	10.00/17.50
Relish, 3 Part,	
7½" Footed..........	12.00/-----
Salt & Pepper, Footed, Pr.	42.50/-----
Sandwich Server,	
Center Handle	900.00/-----
Saucer With Cup Ring ...	32.50/-----
Saucer 6" (Sherbet Plate)	2.50/1.75
Sherbet, 3 1/8".........	7.50/15.00
Sherbet, 4 7/8".........	17.50/20.00

	Green/Yellow
Sugar, 3¼"	8.50/7.50
Sugar, 4¼"	12.00/-----
Tumbler, 3¾", 5 oz. Juice	15.00/-----
Tumbler, 4", 9 oz. Water .	13.00/-----
Tumbler, 4¾, 10 oz. Flat .	15.00/-----
Tumbler, 5", 11 oz. Flat ..	15.00/22.00
Tumbler, 5¼", 15 oz.....	25.00/-----
Tumbler, 3 oz.	
Footed, Juice	32.50/-----
Tumbler, 5", 9 oz. Footed	14.00/12.00
Tumbler, 5¾",	
11 oz. Footed.........	22.50/-----
Vase, 5¾"	75.00/-----
Vase, 8"	15.00/-----
Water Bottle (Dark	
Green) Whitehouse	
Vinegar	17.50/-----

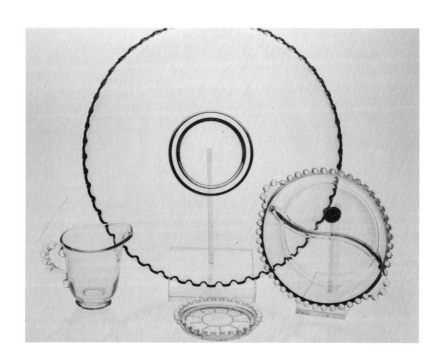

CANDLEWICK
(crystal)
IMPERIAL GLASS COMPANY 1936 to date

	Crystal
Ashtray, 4½"	5.00
Bon Bon, 5", 2 Handle ...	6.00
Bowl, 5", Fruit	4.00
Bowl, 5½", Fruit	4.25
Bowl, 6" Deep	6.50
Bowl, 6", Three Toed	7.50
Bowl, 8½"	10.00
Bowl, 4¾", 2 Handle	6.00
Bowl, 6", 2 Handle	7.00
Bowl, 7", 2 Handle	8.50
Bowl, 8½", 2 Handle	9.00
Bowl, 10", 2 Handle	10.00
Bowl, 10" Float	12.50
Bowl, Punch Set (15 pieces)	75.00
Butter, ¼ lb.	12.50
Cake Stand, 11"	15.00
Candleholder, pair	10.00
Candle, 1 handle pair ...	10.00
Candy & Cover	20.00
Cheese & Cracker Set ...	13.50
Coaster, 4½"	4.50

	Crystal
Compote, 5½", Low Footed	10.00
Creamer, Sugar & Tray ..	12.50
Cup, Coffee	4.00
Cup, Tea	4.00
Jelly, 6" divided, 2 handle	7.50
Marmalade, 2 piece	11.00
Mayonnaise, 2 piece	12.50
Nut, 6", Handled	7.50
Pickle, 8", Oval	8.00
Plate, 6", Bread & Butter .	3.00
Plate, 7", Salad	5.00
Plate, 8"	7.00
Plate, 10", Dinner	8.50
Plate, 12½"	10.00
Plate, 17", Torte	12.50
Plate, 5½", 2 Handle	4.00
Plate, 7", 2 Handle	5.50
Plate, 8½", 2 Handle	7.50
Plate, 10", 2 Handle	9.00
Plate, 12", 2 Handle	12.00
Plate, 10", 2 Handle, Crimped	12.50

	Crystal		Crystal
Relish, 6½" Divided	5.00	Salt & Pepper, pair,	
Relish, 8" Divided	8.00	2 sizes	12.50
Relish, 8½", 4 pint	9.00	Saucer	1.50
Relish, 10½", Oval	10.00	Sherbet, Low, Footed . . .	4.00
Relish, 10½", 5 pint	12.50	Tray, 6½", Oblong	6.00
		Vase, 7"	20.00
		Vase, 8", Fan	22.50

CHERRY BLOSSOM
(See Reproduction Section, Page 147)
(pink, green, delphite, crystal)
JEANNETTE GLASS COMPANY 1930-1939

	Pink/Green		Pink/Green
Bowl, 4¾" Berry	7.00/8.25	Platter, 9" Oval	500.00/-----
Bowl, 5¾" Cereal	18.00/17.50	Platter, 11" Oval	14.00/18.50
Bowl, 7¾" Flat Soup	27.50/32.50	Platter, 13" & 13" Divided	27.50/32.50
Bowl, 8½" Round Berry	11.00/14.00	Salt and Pepper	
Bowl, 9" Oval Vegetable	13.00/16.00	Scalloped Bottom	1000.00/700.00
Bowl, 9" 2 Handled	13.00/14.00	Saucer	3.50/3.00
Bowl, 10½", 3 Leg Fruit	30.00/33.00	Sherbet	8.00/9.50
Butter Dish and Cover	55.00/70.00	Sugar	7.50/8.00
Cake Plate (3 Legs) 10¼"	13.00/15.00	Sugar Cover	10.00/10.00
Coaster	9.50/8.00	Tray, 10½" Sandwich,	
Creamer	9.00/10.00	2 Handled	11.00/13.00
Cup	11.00/12.50	Tumbler, 3¾", 4 oz.	
Mug, 7 oz.	115.00/125.00	Footed, AOP, Round or	
Pitcher, 6¾" AOP,		Scalloped	10.00/14.00
36 oz. Scalloped or		Tumbler, 4½", 9 oz.	
Round Bottom	27.50/35.00	Round Foot AOP	20.00/24.00
Pitcher, 8" PAT, 36 oz. Ftd.	27.00/35.00	Tumbler, 4½", 8 oz.	
Pitcher, 8" PAT, 42 oz. Flat	26.00/30.00	Scalloped Foot AOP	20.00/24.00
Plate, 6" Sherbet	3.75/4.25	Tumbler, 3½",	
Plate, 7" Salad	11.00/11.00	4 oz. Flat PAT	11.00/11.00
Plate, 9" Dinner	9.50/12.00	Tumbler, 4¼",	
Plate, 9" Grill	12.50/12.50	9 oz. Flat PAT	11.00/15.00

	Pink/Green
Tumbler, 5",	
12 oz. Flat PAT	22.50/25.00

Cherry Blossom — Child's Junior Dinner Set

	Pink
Creamer	20.00
Sugar	20.00
Original Box	10.00
Plate, 6"...............	6.50
Cup	15.00
Saucer	4.00
14 Piece Set	137.50

CHINEX CLASSIC
(ivory, ivory decorated)
MACBETH-EVANS DIVISION OF CORNING GLASS WORKS
Late 1930 - Early 1940's

	Ivory/Decorated		Ivory/Decorated
Bowl, 5¾" Cereal	3.00/4.00	Plate, 9¾" Dinner	3.00/4.50
Bowl, 7" Flat Soup	6.00/7.00	Plate, 11½" Sandwich	
Bowl, 9" Vegetable	9.00/12.00	or Cake	6.00/8.00
Butter Dish	40.00/60.00	Saucer	1.50/2.00
Creamer	4.00/6.00	Sherbet, Low Footed	6.00/9.00
Cup	3.00/4.00	Sugar, Open	4.00/6.00
Plate, 6¼" Sherbet	2.00/2.50		

CHRISTMAS CANDY
(teal)
INDIANA GLASS COMPANY 1950's

Creamer	6.00	Plate, 8¼" Luncheon	4.00
Cup	3.00	Saucer	1.50
Plate, 6" Bread & Butter .	1.50	Sugar	6.00

CIRCLE
(green)
HOCKING GLASS COMPANY 1930's

	Green
Creamer	3.50
Cup	2.50
Decanter, Handled	15.00
Goblet, 4½" Wine	1.50
Pitcher, 80 oz.	15.00
Plate, 6" Sherbet	1.50

	Green
Saucer	1.00
Sherbet	3.00
Sugar	3.50
Tumbler, 4 oz. Juice	3.00
Tumbler, 8 oz. Water	3.50
Vase, Hat Shape	15.00

CLOVERLEAF
(pink, green, yellow, black)
HAZEL ATLAS GLASS COMPANY   1930-1936

	Green/Yellow
Ash Tray 4", Match Holder in Center (black)	45.00
Ash Tray 5¾", Match Holder in Center (black)	60.00
Bowl, 4" Dessert	8.00/12.00
Bowl, 5" Cereal	7.50/15.00
Bowl, 7" Salad	15.00/32.50
Candy Dish and Cover	30.00/75.00
Creamer, Footed 3-5/8"	6.00/10.00
Cup	4.00/6.00
Plate, 6" Sherbet	3.00/4.50

	Green/Yellow
Plate, 8" Luncheon	3.50/5.00
Plate, 10¼" Grill	1.50/10.00
Salt and Pepper, Pair	20.00/75.00
Saucer	2.00/2.50
Sherbet, 3" Footed	4.00/7.00
Sugar, Footed, 3-5/8"	5.00/8.00
Tumbler, 4", 9 oz. Flat	17.50/-----
Tumbler, 3¾", 10 oz. Flat	15.00/-----
Tumbler, 5¾", 10 oz. Footed	13.00/17.50

COLONIAL, "KNIFE AND FORK"
(pink, green, crystal)
HOCKING GLASS COMPANY 1934-1938

	Pink/Green
Bowl, 3¾"	15.00/20.00
Bowl, 4½" Berry	4.50/6.50
Bowl, 5½" Cereal	15.00/25.00
Bowl, 4½" Cream Soup . .	25.00/25.00
Bowl, 7" Low Soup	18.00/27.50
Bowl, 9" Large Berry	7.00/10.00
Bowl, 10" Oval Vegetable	10.00/12.00
Butter Dish And Cover . . .	400.00/37.50
Creamer, 5", 8 oz.	
(Milk Pitcher)	10.00/12.00
Cup	° 4.50/7.50
Goblet, 3¾", 1 oz. Cordial	-----/18.00
Goblet, 4" 3 oz. Cocktail .	-----/15.00
Goblet, 4½", 2½ oz.	
Wine	-----/17.50
Goblet, 5¼", 4 oz. Claret	-----/17.50
Goblet, 5¾", 8½" oz.	
Water	18.00/15.00
Mug, 4½", 12 oz.	100.00/300.00
Pitcher, 7", 54 oz. Ice Lip	
or None	25.00/30.00

	Pink/Green
Pitcher, 7¾", 68 oz.	
Ice Lip or None	25.00/40.00
Plate, 6" Sherbet	2.00/2.50
Plate, 8½" Luncheon	3.75/4.00
Plate, 10" Dinner	15.00/30.00
Plate, 10" Grill	10.00/15.00
Platter, 12" Oval	9.00/11.00
Salt and Pepper, Pair	90.00/95.00
Saucer (Same as	
sherbet plate)	2.00/2.50
Sherbet	5.00/7.50
Spoon Holder or Celery . .	60.00/70.00
Sugar, 5"	8.00/9.00
Sugar Cover	12.50/9.00
Tumbler, 3", 5 oz. Juice . .	7.00/10.00
Tumbler, 4", 9 oz. Water .	6.50/11.00
Tumbler, 10 oz.	10.00/15.00
Tumbler, 12 oz. Iced Tea .	15.00/22.00
Tumbler, 15 oz.	
Lemonade	20.00/32.50

	Pink/Green		Pink/Green
Tumbler, 3¼", 3 oz.		Tumbler, 5¼", 10 oz. Ftd.	10.00/16.00
Footed	8.00/12.50	Whiskey, 2½", 1½ oz. . .	6.00/8.00
Tumbler, 4", 5 oz. Footed	12.00/18.00		

COLONIAL BLOCK
(green)
HAZEL ATLAS GLASS COMPANY Late 1920's, Early 1930's

	Green		Green
Bowl, 4"	3.00	Creamer	6.00
Bowl, 7"	7.00	Sugar	4.00
Butter Dish	27.50	Sugar Cover	3.50
Candy Dish & Cover, 8½"	17.50		

COLONIAL FLUTED, "ROPE"
(green, crystal)
FEDERAL GLASS COMPANY 1928-1933

	Green		Green
Bowl, 4" Berry	3.00	Plate, 8" Luncheon	2.50
Bowl, 6" Cereal	4.00	Plate, 9½"	6.00
Bowl, 6½" Deep Salad . .	7.50	Saucer	1.25
Bowl, 7½" Large Berry . .	7.50	Sherbet	3.50
Creamer	3.50	Sugar	2.50
Cup	2.75	Sugar Cover	4.00
Plate, 6" Sherbet	1.25		

COLUMBIA
(crystal, pink)
FEDERAL GLASS COMPANY 1938-1942

	Crystal/Pink		Crystal/Pink
Bowl, 5" Cereal	5.00/----	Cup	3.00/6.50
Bowl, 8" Low Soup	6.50/----	Plate, 6" Bread & Butter	1.50/3.00
Bowl, 8½" Salad	6.00/----	Plate, 9½" Luncheon	3.00/10.00
Bowl, 10½" Ruffled Edge	9.00/----	Plate, 11¾" Chop	5.00/----
Butter Dish and Cover		Saucer	1.00/4.00
Ruby Flashed		Snack Plate	4.00/----
(10.00/15.00)	15.00/----		

CORONATION, "BANDED FINE RIB", "SAXON"
(pink, crystal, royal ruby)
HOCKING GLASS COMPANY 1936-1940

	Pink/Red		Pink/Red
Bowl, 4¼" Berry	2.75/4.00	Plate, 8½" Luncheon	3.25/5.00
Bowl, 6½" Nappy	3.00/6.00	Saucer	1.50/----
Bowl, 8" Large Berry	6.00/9.00	Sherbet	2.50/----
Cup	3.00/4.00	Tumbler, 5",	
Plate, 6" Sherbet	1.50/----	10 oz. Footed	6.50/----

CREMAX
(cremax, decal decorations)
MACBETH-EVANS DIVISION OF CORNING GLASS WORKS
Late 1930's - Early 1940's

	Ivory/Ivory Decorated		Ivory/Ivory Decorated
Bowl, 5¾" Cereal	2.50/3.00	Plate, 6¼" Bread and Butter	1.25/2.00
Bowl, 9" Vegetable	5.00/7.00	Plate, 9¾" Dinner	3.00/4.00
Creamer	3.00/5.00	Plate, 11½" Sandwich . . .	3.00/4.00
Cup	2.50/3.00	Saucer	1.00/1.50
		Sugar, Open	3.00/5.00

CUBE, "CUBIST"
(pink, green, crystal)
JEANNETTE GLASS COMPANY 1929-1933

	Pink/Green		Pink/Green
Bowl, 4½" Dessert	3.00/3.50	Plate, 6" Sherbet	1.25/2.00
Bowl, 4½" Deep	3.25/----	Plate, 8" Luncheon	2.00/3.00
Bowl, 6½" Salad	5.00/9.00	Powder Jar and Cover,	
Butter Dish and Cover	40.00/40.00	3 Legs	9.00/12.00
Candy Jar and Cover,		Salt and Pepper, Pr.	17.50/20.00
6½"	17.00/20.00	Saucer	1.00/1.50
Coaster, 3¼"	2.50/3.50	Sherbet, Footed	3.50/4.50
Creamer, 2"	2.00/----	Sugar, 2"	2.00/----
Creamer, 3"	3.00/4.00	Sugar, 3"	2.50/4.00
Cup	3.00/4.00	Sugar/Candy Cover	5.00/6.00
Pitcher, 8¾", 45 oz.	100.00/125.00	Tumbler, 4", 9 oz.	15.00/25.00

"DAISY", NUMBER 620
(crystal, 1933; amber, 1940; dark green and milk glass, 1960's)
INDIANA GLASS COMPANY

	Crystal/Amber		Crystal/Amber
Bowl, 4½", Berry	2.00/6.00	Plate, 9-3/8" Dinner	2.50/4.00
Bowl, 4½" Cream Soup . .	3.00/6.00	Plate, 10-3/8" Grill	4.00/7.00
Bowl, 6" Cereal	5.00/15.00	Plate, 11½" Cake or	
Bowl, 7-3/8" Deep Berry .	3.00/6.00	Sandwich	5.00/6.00
Bowl, 9-3/8" Deep Berry .	6.00/18.00	Platter, 10¾"	5.00/9.00
Bowl, 10" Oval Vegetable	5.00/11.00	Relish Dish, 3 Part, 8-3/8"	8.00/12.00
Creamer, Footed	2.50/4.00	Saucer	.75/1.25
Cup	2.00/3.25	Sherbet, Footed	3.00/5.00
Plate, 6" Sherbet	1.00/2.00	Sugar, Footed	2.50/4.00
Plate, 7-3/8" Salad	2.00/5.00	Tumbler, 9 oz. Footed . . .	5.00/10.00
Plate, 8-3/8" Luncheon . .	2.00/5.50	Tumbler, 12 oz. Footed . .	9.00/22.00

DIAMOND QUILTED, "FLAT DIAMOND"
(pink, blue, green, crystal, black)
IMPERIAL GLASS COMPANY Late 1920's - Early 1930's

	Green/Blue
Bowl, 4¾" Cream Soup . .	6.00/9.00
Bowl, 5" Cereal	3.50/6.00
Bowl, 5½", One Handle .	5.00/7.50
Bowl, 7" Crimped Edge . .	5.00/8.00
Bowl, Rolled Edge	
Console	12.00/20.00
Cake Salver, Tall 10"	
Diameter	25.00/-----
Candlesticks (2 Styles) Pr.	8.00/15.00
Candy Jar and Cover,	
Footed	12.00/20.00
Compote and Cover,	
11½"	30.00/-----
Creamer	5.00/8.00

	Green/Blue
Cup	2.00/5.00
Goblet, 1 oz. Cordial	4.50/-----
Goblet, 2 oz. Wine	4.50/-----
Goblet, 3 oz. Wine	5.50/-----
Goblet, 6" 9 oz.	
Champagne	7.00/-----
Ice Bucket	35.00/50.00
Mayonnaise Set: Ladle,	
Plate, 3 Footed Dish . . .	12.50/-----
Pitcher, 64 oz.	20.00/-----
Plate, 6" Sherbet	1.50/2.50
Plate, 7" Salad	3.00/5.00
Plate, 8" Luncheon	3.00/6.00
Plate, 14" Sandwich	8.00/-----

	Green/Blue
Sandwich Server,	
Center Handle	12.00/-----
Saucer	1.50/2.50
Sherbet	3.50/7.50
Sugar	5.00/8.00
Tumbler, 9 oz. Water	4.50/-----

	Green/Blue
Tumbler, 12 oz. Iced Tea .	6.00/-----
Tumbler, 6 oz. Footed ...	4.50/-----
Tumbler, 9 oz. Footed ...	7.50/-----
Tumbler, 12 oz. Footed ..	9.50/-----
Whiskey, 1½ oz.	5.00/-----

DIANA
(pink, amber, crystal)
FEDERAL GLASS COMPANY 1937-1941

	Pink/Amber		Pink/Amber
Ash Tray, 3½"	2.50/-----	Cup, Demi-tasse, 2 oz. &	
Bowl, 5" Cereal	3.00/3.00	4½" Saucer Set	4.00/-----
Bowl, 5½" Cream Soup . .	4.00/4.50	Plate, 5½" Child's	2.50/-----
Bowl, 9" Salad	6.25/5.00	Plate, 6" Bread & Butter .	1.00/1.25
Bowl, 11" Console Fruit . .	6.00/8.00	Plate, 9½" Dinner	3.00/4.00
Bowl, 12" Scalloped Edge	7.00/8.00	Plate, 11¾" Sandwich . . .	4.00/5.50
Candy Jar & Cover, Round	16.00/25.00	Platter, 12" Oval	5.00/6.00
Coaster, 3½"	3.00/-----	Salt & Pepper, Pr.	25.00/60.00
Creamer, Oval	3.00/3.50	Saucer	1.50/1.25
Cup	3.50/4.00	Sherbet	3.00/3.00
		Sugar, Open, Oval	3.00/3.50
		Tumbler, 4-1/8", 9 oz. . . .	6.00/8.00

DOGWOOD, "APPLE BLOSSOM", "WILD ROSE"
(pink, green)
MACBETH-EVANS GLASS COMPANY 1929-1932

	Pink/Green		Pink/Green
Bowl, 5½" Cereal	11.00/12.50	Plate, 9¼" Dinner	12.50/-----
Bowl, 8½" Berry	25.00/50.00	Plate, 10½" Grill AOP	
Bowl, 10¼" Fruit	90.00/75.00	or Border Design Only	11.00/9.00
Cake Plate, 11" Heavy		Plate, 12" Salver	15.00/-----
Solid Foot	100.00/-----	Platter, 12" Oval (Rare)	165.00/-----
Cake Plate, 13" Heavy		Saucer	3.00/4.00
Solid Foot	50.00/45.00	Sherbet, Low Footed	15.00/30.00
Creamer, 2½" Thin	7.50/30.00	Sugar, 2½", Thin	6.00/30.00
Creamer, 3¼" Thick	12.00/-----	Sugar, 3¼", Thick	6.00/-----
Cup, Thin or Thick	6.00/12.50	Tumbler, 3½", 5 oz.	
Pitcher, 8", 80 oz.		Decorated	60.00/-----
Decorated	90.00/400.00	Tumbler, 4" 10 oz.	
Pitcher, 8", 80 oz.		Decorated	17.00/40.00
(American Sweetheart		Tumbler, 4¾", 11 oz.	
Style)	425.00/-----	Decorated	22.00/45.00
Plate, 6" Bread and		Tumbler, 5", 12 oz.	
Butter	3.00/3.00	Decorated	25.00/50.00
Plate, 8" Luncheon	3.00/3.50		

DORIC
(pink, green)
JEANNETTE GLASS COMPANY 1935-1938

	Pink/Green
Bowl, 4½" Berry	3.25/4.25
Bowl, 5" Cream Soup	-----/100.00
Bowl, 5½" Cereal	12.00/15.00
Bowl, 8¼" Large Berry . .	8.00/9.00
Bowl, 9" Two Handled . . .	9.00/9.00
Bowl, 9" Oval Vegetable .	9.00/10.00
Butter Dish and Cover . . .	50.00/60.00
Cake Plate, 10", Three Legs	10.00/9.00
Candy Dish and Cover, 8"	20.00/21.00
Candy Dish, Three Part . .	4.00/4.50
Coaster, 3"	8.00/10.00
Creamer, 4"	6.50/8.00
Cup	4.50/5.00
Pitcher, 6", 36 oz. Flat . . .	22.00/27.00
Pitcher, 7½", 48 oz. Footed	190.00/350.00

	Pink/Green
Plate, 6" Sherbet	2.35/2.50
Plate, 7" Salad	10.00/9.00
Plate, 9" Dinner	5.50/7.00
Plate, 9" Grill	6.00/9.00
Platter, 12" Oval	9.00/9.50
Relish Tray, 4" x 4"	4.00/6.00
Relish Tray, 4" x 8"	5.00/8.00
Salt and Pepper, Pr.	22.50/27.00
Saucer	2.00/2.00
Sherbet, Footed	5.50/7.00
Sugar	7.00/7.50
Sugar Cover	8.00/10.00
Tray, 10" Handled	6.00/9.00
Tray, 8" x 8" Serving	7.00/8.00
Tumbler, 4½", 9 oz. Flat .	18.00/25.00
Tumbler, 4", 11 oz. Ftd. . .	13.00/17.00
Tumbler, 5", 12 oz. Ftd. . .	14.00/18.00

DORIC and PANSY
(pink, crystal, ultramarine)
JEANNETTE GLASS COMPANY 1937-1938

	Pink/Ultra-marine
Bowl, 4½" Berry	6.00/7.50
Bowl, 8" Large Berry	15.00/50.00
Bowl, 9" Handled	----/20.00
Butter Dish and Cover	----/650.00
Cup	----/10.00
Creamer	----/150.00
Plate, 6" Sherbet	6.00/8.00
Plate, 7" Salad	-----/22.50
Plate, 9" Dinner	----/13.00
Salt and Pepper, Pr.	-----/350.00
Saucer	----/3.50
Sugar, Open	----/150.00
Tray, 10" Handled	----/15.00
Tumbler, 4½", 9 oz.	----/32.50

DORIC AND PANSY
"PRETTY POLLY PARTY DISHES"

	Pink/Ultra-marine
Cup	15.00/20.00
Saucer	3.00/4.00
Plate	6.00/8.00
Creamer	20.00/30.00
Sugar	20.00/30.00
14 Piece Set	140.00/175.00

ENGLISH HOBNAIL
(crystal, pink, amber, turquoise, cobalt, green)
WESTMORELAND GLASS COMPANY 1920's-1970's

	Pink or Green		Pink or Green
Ash Tray, Several Shapes	17.50	Cigarette Box	18.00
Bowls, 4½", 5" Square		Cologne Bottle	20.00
and Round	8.00	Creamer, Footed or Flat .	12.50
Bowl, Cream Soup	10.00	Cup	10.00
Bowls, 6", Several Styles .	9.00	Decanter, 20 oz.	
Bowls, 8", Several Styles .	15.00	with Stopper	50.00
Bowls, 8", Footed and		Demitasse Cup & Saucer .	20.00
Two Handled	35.00	Egg Cup	20.00
Bowls, 11" and 12"		Goblet, 1 oz. Cordial	15.00
Nappies	30.00	Goblet, 2 oz. Wine	12.00
Bowls, Relish, Oval,		Goblet, 3 oz. Cocktail . . .	12.00
8", 9"	15.00	Goblet, 5 oz. Claret	12.50
Bowl, Relish, Oval, 12" . .	15.00	Goblet, 6¼", 8 oz.	15.00
Candlesticks, 3½", Pair .	25.00	Grapefruit, 6½",	
Candlesticks, 8½", Pair .	40.00	Flange Rim	10.00
Candy Dish, ½ lb.,		Lamp, 6¼", Electric	50.00
Cone Shaped	40.00	Lamp, 9¼"	75.00
Candy Dish and Cover,		Marmalade and Cover . . .	25.00
Three Feet	50.00	Pitcher, 23 oz.	75.00
Celery Dish, 9"	15.00	Pitcher, 39 oz.	90.00
Celery Dish 12"	17.50	Pitcher, 60 oz.	125.00

	Pink or Green		Pink or Green
Pitcher, ½ Gal.		Sugar, Footed or Flat	12.50
Straight Sides	135.00	Tumbler, 3¾",	
Plate, 5½", 6½", Sherbet	3.00	5 oz. or 8 oz.	10.00
Plate, 7¼", Pie	3.50	Tumbler, 4", 10 oz.	
Plate, 8" Round or Square	6.00	Iced Tea	12.50
Plate, 10" Dinner	15.00	Tumbler, 5", 12 oz.	
Salt and Pepper, Pr.,		Iced Tea	15.00
Round or Square Bases	50.00	Tumbler, 7 oz., Footed . .	12.00
Salt Dip, 2", Footed and		Tumbler, 9 oz., Footed . .	13.00
with Place Card Holder	12.50	Tumbler, 12½ oz. Footed	17.00
Saucer	3.00	Whiskey, 1½ oz. & 3 oz. .	15.00
Sherbet	10.00		

FIRE-KING DINNERWARE
("Philbe", blue, pink, green and crystal)
ANCHOR HOCKING GLASS COMPANY 1937-1938

	All Colors		All Colors
Bowl, 5½" Cereal	20.00	Plate, 10½" Savler	15.00
Bowl, 7¼" Salad	30.00	Plate, 10½" Grill	15.00
Bowl, 10" Oval Vegetable	25.00	Plate, 11-5/8" Salver	20.00
Candy Jar, 4" Low,		Platter, 12" Closed	
with Cover	95.00	Handles	30.00
Cookie Jar with Cover . . .	150.00	Saucer, 6"	
Creamer, 3¼" Ftd	25.00	(same as sherbet)	15.00
Cup	45.00	Sugar, 3¼" Ftd.	25.00
Goblet, 7¼" thin, 9 oz . . .	100.00	Tumbler, 4",	
Pitcher, 6" Juice, 36 oz . . .	250.00	9 oz. Flat Water	75.00
Pitcher, 8½", 80 oz	300.00	Tumbler, 3½" Ftd. Juice .	75.00
Plate, 6" Sherbet	15.00	Tumbler, 5¼" Ftd., 10 oz.	35.00
Plate, 8" Luncheon	18.00	Tumbler, 6½" Ftd.,	
Plate, 10"		15 oz. Iced Tea	25.00
Heavy Sandwich	20.00		

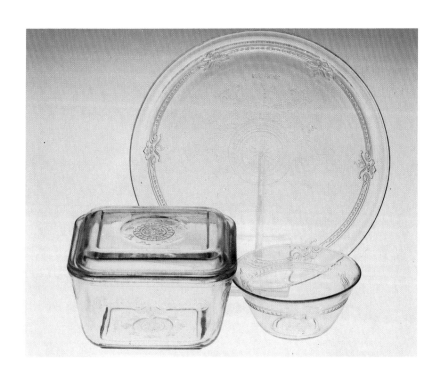

FIRE-KING OVEN GLASS
(blue, 1940's; crystal, 1950's)
ANCHOR HOCKING GLASS COMPANY

	Blue		Blue
Baker, 1 pt., rd. or sq. . . .	2.50	Casserole, 10 oz., Tab Handle Cover	6.00
Baker, 1 qt.	3.00	Coffee Mug, 7 oz.	10.00
Baker, 1½ qt.	3.50	Cup, 8 oz. Measuring	4.00
Baker, 2 qt.	4.50	Custard Cup, 5 oz.	2.00
Cake Pan (deep), 8¾ " . . .	7.50	Custard Cup, 6 oz., 2 Styles	2.00
Casserole, 1 pt., Knob Handle Cover . . .	4.00	Loaf Pan, 9-1/8", Deep . .	5.00
Casserole, 1 qt., Knob Handle Cover . . .	5.00	Nurser, 4 oz.	2.00
Casserole, 1½ qt., Knob Handle Cover . . .	7.00	Nurser, 8 oz.	3.00
Casserole, 2 qt., Knob Handle Cover . . .	9.00	Pie Plate, 4-3/8" Individual	2.50
Casserole, 1 qt., Pie Plate Cover	6.00	Pie Plate, 5-3/8" Deep Dish	3.00
Casserole, 1½ qt., Pie Plate Cover	9.00	Pie Plate, 8-3/8"	3.00
Casserole, 2 qt., Pie Plate Cover	12.50	Pie Plate, 9"	4.00
		Pie Plate, 9-5/8"	4.00
		Pie Plate, 10-3/8" Juice Saver . . .	9.00
		Perculator Top, 2-1/8" . . .	2.00
		Refrigerator Jar & Cover, 4½"x5"	4.00

	Blue		Blue
Refrigerator Jar & Cover, 5-1/8"x9-1/8" . .	9.00	Utility Pan, 10½", Rectangular	5.00
Table Server, Tab Handles (Hot Plate) . . .	7.00	Utility Pan, 8-1/8"x12-1/2"	6.00

FLORAGOLD, "LOUISA"
(iridescent, shell pink, crystal)
JEANNETTE GLASS COMPANY 1950's

	Iridescent		Iridescent
Bowl, 4½" Square	3.00	Creamer	4.00
Bowl, 5½" Cereal Round.	15.00	Cup	3.00
Bowl, 5½" Ruffled Fruit..	3.00	Pitcher, 64 oz..........	17.50
Bowl, 8½" Ruffled Fruit..	4.00	Plate, 5¾" Sherbet	4.50
Bowl, 9½" Salad, Deep ..	20.00	Plate, 8½" Dinner	11.50
Bowl, 12" Ruffled,		Plate or Tray, 13½"	10.00
Large Fruit...........	6.00	Indent on 13½" Plate..	27.50
Butter Dish and Cover		Platter, 11¼"	10.00
¼ lb. Oblong	13.00	Salt and Pepper,	
Butter Dish and		Plastic Tops	27.50
Cover, Round	30.00	Saucer	4.50
Candlesticks, Double		Sherbet, Low Footed	6.50
Branch, Pr.	25.00	Sugar	3.00
Candy or Cheese Dish		Sugar Lid	3.50
and Cover, 6¾"	25.00	Tumbler, 10 oz., Footed .	8.00
Candy, 5¼" Long, 4 Feet.	4.00	Tumbler, 11 oz., Footed .	10.00
Coaster—Ash Tray, 4"...	4.00	Tumbler, 15 oz., Footed .	25.00

FLORAL "POINSETTA"
(pink, green, delphite)
JEANNETTE GLASS COMPANY 1931-1935

	Pink/Green
Bowl, 4" Berry	7.00/7.50
Bowl, 5½" Cream Soup	-----/200.00
Bowl, 7½" Salad	8.00/9.50
Bowl, 8" Covered Vegetable	19.00/20.00
Bowl, 9" Oval Vegetable	8.00/9.00
Butter Dish and Cover	55.00/65.00
Candlesticks, 4" Pr.	35.00/50.00
Candy Jar and Cover	20.00/22.50
Creamer, Flat	7.00/7.00
Coaster, 3¼"	5.00/6.00
Compote, 9"	175.00/200.00
Cup	6.00/6.00
Ice Tub, Oval, 3½" High	250.00/300.00
Lamp	75.00/75.00
Pitcher, 5½", 23 or 24 oz. Flat	-----/400.00
Pitcher, 8", 32 oz. Footed Cone	16.00/20.00
Pitcher, 10¼", 48 oz. Lemonade	125.00/150.00

	Pink/Green
Plate, 6" Sherbet	2.75/2.75
Plate, 8" Salad	4.50/5.50
Plate, 9" Dinner	8.50/9.00
Plate, 9" Grill	-----/95.00
Platter 10¾" Oval	7.50/9.50
Refrigerator Dish and Cover, 5" Square	-----/35.00
Relish Dish, Oval, Two Part	6.00/7.50
Salt and Pepper, Pr., 4" Footed	26.00/30.00
Salt and Pepper, 6" Flat (pink)	25.00/-----
Saucer	4.00/5.00
Sherbet	6.50/7.50
Sugar	6.00/6.00
Sugar/Candy Cover	7.00/10.00
Tray, 6" Square, Closed Handles	8.00/8.50
Tumbler, 4", 5 oz. Footed Juice	10.00/10.50

	Pink/Green		Pink/Green
Tumbler, 4¾", 7 oz.		Rose Bowl	-----/350.00
Footed Water	8.50/10.50	Vase, 3 Legged Flared	
Tumbler, 5¼", 9 oz.		(Also in Crystal)	-----/350.00
Footed Lemonade	20.00/21.00	Vase, 6¼" Tall	
Vase, 3 Legged		(8 Sided).............	-----/350.00

FLORAL AND DIAMOND BAND
(crystal, pink, green)
U.S. GLASS COMPANY 1927-1931

	Pink or Green		Pink or Green
Bowl, 4½" Berry	4.00	Pitcher, 8", 42 oz.	60.00
Bowl, 5¾" Nappy, Handled	5.50	Plate, 8" Luncheon	10.50
		Sherbet	3.50
Bowl, 8" Large Berry	8.00	Sugar, Small	5.00
Butter Dish and Cover	60.00	Sugar, 5¼"	7.00
Compote, 5½" Tall	6.50	Sugar Lid	20.00
Creamer, Small	5.00	Tumbler, 4" Water	7.50
Creamer, 4¾"	9.00	Tumbler, 5" Iced Tea	12.50

FLORENTINE NO. 1, "POPPY NO. 1"
(pink, green, crystal, yellow, cobalt)
HAZEL ATLAS GLASS COMPANY 1934-1936

	Green/Yellow
Ash Tray, 5½"	15.00/23.00
Bowl, 5" Berry	5.00/6.00
Bowl, 6" Cereal.........	7.00/8.50
Bowl, 8½" Large Berry ..	12.00/15.00
Bowl, 9½" Oval	
Vegetable and Cover..	25.00/30.00
Butter Dish and Cover ...	95.00/110.00
Coaster/Ash Tray,	
3¾"	10.00/12.50
Creamer	6.00/8.00
Creamer, Ruffled	15.00/20.00
Cup..................	4.00/5.00
Pitcher, 6½", 36 oz.	
Footed	27.50/35.00
Pitcher, 7½", 54 oz. Flat	
Ice Lip or None	35.00/100.00
Plate, 6" Sherbet	2.50/3.00

	Green/Yellow
Plate, 8½" Salad	4.50/7.00
Plate, 10" Dinner	6.50/9.50
Plate, 10" Grill	7.00/9.00
Platter, 11½" Oval......	7.50/10.00
Salt and Pepper, Footed .	25.00/35.00
Saucer	2.00/3.00
Sherbet, 3 oz. Footed....	3.50/7.00
Sugar	5.00/6.00
Sugar Cover	9.50/9.50
Sugar, Ruffled	13.00/18.00
Tumbler, 3¾", 5 oz.	
Footed Juice	6.50/11.00
Tumbler, 4¾", 10 oz.	
Footed Water	10.00/13.00
Tumbler, 5¼", 12 oz.	
Footed Iced Tea	12.00/17.00

FLORENTINE NO. 2, "POPPY NO. 2"
(pink, green, yellow, crystal, cobalt blue)
HAZEL ATLAS GLASS COMPANY 1932-1935

	Green/Yellow
Bowl, 4½" Berry	6.50/11.00
Bowl, 4¾" Cream Soup	7.50/12.00
Bowl, 6" Cereal	10.00/17.50
Bowl, 8" Large Berry	12.00/14.00
Bowl, 9" Oval	
Vegetable and Cover	25.00/32.50
Butter Dish and Cover	75.00/90.00
Candlesticks, 2¾", Pr.	28.00/32.00
Candy Dish and Cover	60.00/110.00
Coaster, 3¼"	9.00/12.00
Coaster/Ash Tray, 3¾"	10.00/15.00
Coaster/Ash Tray, 5½"	12.00/20.00
Compote, 3½" Ruffled	10.00/----
Creamer	5.00/6.00
Cup	4.50/5.00
Custard Cup or Jello	20.00/35.00
Gravy Boat (yellow)	----/25.00
Pitcher, 7½", 28 oz.	
Cone Footed	15.00/18.00
Pitcher, 7½", 54 oz.	35.00/100.00

	Green/Yellow
Pitcher, 8", 76 oz.	60.00/125.00
Plate, 6" Sherbet	2.00/3.00
Plate, 6¼" with Indent	
for Custard	12.00/20.00
Plate, 8½" Salad	4.00/5.00
Plate, 10" Dinner	6.50/17.50
Plate, 10¼" Grill	6.00/7.00
Platter, 11" Oval	9.00/9.00
Platter, 11½" for	
Gravyboat (yellow)	----/25.00
Relish Dish, 10", 3 Part	
or Plain	7.00/11.00
Salt and Pepper, Pr.	27.50/32.50
Saucer	2.00/2.50
Sherbet, Footed	5.00/7.00
Sugar	4.50/6.00
Sugar Cover	8.00/10.00
Tumbler, 3½", 5 oz.	
Juice	6.00/10.00
Tumbler, 4" 9 oz. Water	8.00/12.00

	Green/Yellow		Green/Yellow
Tumbler, 5" 12 oz.		Tumbler, 4½", 9 oz.	
Iced Tea	10.00/20.00	Footed	9.00/10.00
Tumbler, 3¼" 5 oz.		Tumbler, 5", 12 oz.	
Footed	7.50/7.50	Footed	12.00/20.00
Tumbler, 4", 5 oz. Footed	7.50/9.00	Vase or Parfait, 6"	17.00/35.00

FLOWER GARDEN WITH BUTTERFLIES, "BUTTERFLIES AND ROSES"
(pink, green, blue-green, canary yellow, amber, black)
U.S. GLASS COMPANY Late 1920's

	All Colors		All Colors
Ash Tray,		Cup	75.00
Match-Pack Holders . . .	75.00	Plate, 8", Two Styles	10.00
Bowl, Rolled Edge		Powder Jar, Footed	25.00
Console	45.00	Powder Jar, Flat	20.00
Candlesticks, 4", Pr.	35.00	Sandwich Server,	
Candlesticks, 8", Pr.	55.00	center handle	50.00
Candy Dish and Cover, 8"	40.00	Saucer	35.00
Candy Dish, Open, 6" . . .	15.00	Sugar, Open	30.00
Cheese and Cracker Set		Tray, 5½"x10" Oval	30.00
(4" Compote, 10" Plate)	35.00	Tray, Rectangular,	
Cologne Bottle, 7½",		11¾"x7¾"	30.00
Tall Footed	25.00	Vase, 7" (Black)	75.00
Console Bowl, 10" Footed	35.00	Vase, 10"	65.00
Creamer	30.00		

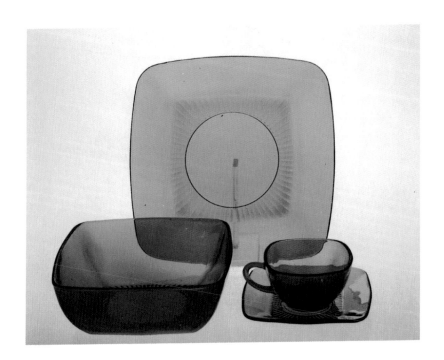

FOREST GREEN
(dark green glass)
ANCHOR HOCKING 1950's-1967

	Green		Green
Ash Tray	2.00	Pitcher, 3 qt., Rnd.	15.00
Bowl, 4¾" Dessert	3.00	Platter, Rectangular	7.00
Bowl, 6" Soup	4.00	Saucer	.75
Bowl, 7-3/8" Salad	5.00	Sugar, Flat	2.50
Creamer, Flat	2.50	Tumbler, 5 oz.	1.50
Cup	2.00	Tumbler, 10 oz.	2.50
Plate, 6-5/8" Salad	1.00	Vase, 4" Ivy	2.00
Plate, 8-3/8" Luncheon .	2.50	Vase 6-3/8"	3.00
Plate, 9¼" Dinner	6.00	Vase, 9"	3.00

"FORTUNE"
(pink, crystal)
HOCKING GLASS COMPANY 1937-1938

	Pink		Pink
Bowl, 4" Berry	2.50	Candy Dish and Cover,	
Bowl, 4½" Dessert	3.25	Flat	10.00
Bowl, 4½" Handled	3.25	Cup	3.00
Bowl, 5¼" Rolled Edge	3.50	Plate, 6" Sherbet	2.00
Bowl, 7¾" Salad or		Plate, 8" Luncheon	4.00
Large Berry	4.00	Saucer	2.00
		Tumbler, 3½", 5 oz. Juice	3.00
		Tumbler, 4", 9 oz. Water	4.00

"FRUITS"
(pink, green, crystal)
HAZEL ATLAS AND OTHER GLASS COMPANIES 1931-1953

	Pink or Green		Pink or Green
Bowl, 5" Cereal	10.00	Sherbet	5.00
Bowl, 8" Berry	30.00	Tumbler, 3½", Juice	5.00
Cup	3.50	Tumbler, 4" (One Fruit)	7.50
Pitcher, 7" Flat Bottom	35.00	Tumbler, 4"	
Plate, 8" Luncheon	3.50	(Combination of Fruits)	8.00
Saucer	2.00		

GEORGIAN, "LOVEBIRDS"
(green, crystal)
FEDERAL GLASS COMPANY 1931-1936

	Green		Green
Bowl, 4½" Berry	4.25	Hot Plate, 5" Center Design	25.00
Bowl, 5¾" Cereal	8.00	Plate, 6" Sherbet	2.50
Bowl, 6½" Deep	30.00	Plate, 8" Luncheon	5.00
Bowl, 7½" Large Berry	23.00	Plate, 9¼" Dinner	13.00
Bowl, 9" Oval Vegetable	32.50	Plate, 9¼" Center Design Only	10.00
Butter Dish and Cover	52.50	Platter, 11½" Closed Handled	32.50
Cold Cuts Server, 18½" Wood with Seven 5" Openings for 5" Coasters	375.00	Saucer	2.00
Creamer, 3" Footed	6.50	Sherbet	6.00
Creamer, 4" Footed	8.00	Sugar, 3" Footed	5.00
Cup	5.00	Sugar, 4" Footed	7.00
		Sugar Cover	10.00
		Tumbler, 4", 9 oz. Flat	25.00
		Tumbler, 5¼", 12 oz. Flat	35.00

HARP
JEANNETTE GLASS COMPANY 1954-1957
Crystal and crystal with gold rims.

	Crystal		Crystal
Ash Tray/Coaster	2.00	Plate, 7"	2.00
Coaster	1.50	Saucer	1.00
Cup	2.00	Tray, Rectangular	12.00
Cake Stand, 9"	7.50	Vase, 6"	6.00

HERITAGE
(crystal, pink, blue, green)
FEDERAL GLASS COMPANY Late 1930's-1960's

	Crystal		Crystal
Bowl, 5" Berry	3.50	Plate, 8" Luncheon	4.00
Bowl, 8½" Large Berry . .	10.00	Plate, 9¼" Dinner	4.50
Bowl, 10½", Fruit	8.00	Plate 12" Sandwich	5.00
Cup	2.50	Saucer	2.00
Creamer, Footed	6.50	Sugar, Open, Footed	6.50

HEX OPTIC, "HONEYCOMB"
(pink, green)
JEANNETTE GLASS COMPANY 1928-1932

	Pink or Green		Pink or Green
Bowl, 4¼" Berry, Ruffled	2.00	Plate, 8" Luncheon	4.50
Bowl, 7½" Large Berry . .	4.50	Platter, 11" Round	4.00
Butter Dish and Cover,		Refrigerator Dish	4.00
Rectangular 1 Lb. Size .	15.00	Salt and Pepper, Pr.	15.00
Creamer, 2 Style Handles	2.50	Saucer	1.50
Cup, 2 Style Handles	2.50	Sugar, 2 Styles of Handles	2.50
Ice Bucket, Metal Handle	7.50	Sherbet, 5 oz. Footed. . . .	3.00
Pitcher, 5", 32 oz.		Tumbler, 3¾", 9 oz.	3.50
Sunflower Motif		Tumbler, 5¾", Footed . . .	4.00
in Bottom	10.00	Tumbler, 7" Footed	5.00
Pitcher, 9", 48 oz. Footed	25.00	Whiskey, 2", 1 oz.	3.00
Plate, 6" Sherbet	1.25		

71

HOBNAIL
(crystal, pink)
HOCKING GLASS COMPANY 1934-1936

	Crystal		Crystal
Bowl, 5½" Cereal	2.50	Sugar, Footed	2.00
Cup	1.75	Tumbler, 5 oz. Juice	3.00
Creamer, Footed	2.00	Tumbler, 9 oz., 10 oz.	
Decanter and Stopper,		Water	4.75
32 oz.	12.50	Tumbler, 15 oz.	
Goblet, 10 oz. Water	4.00	Iced Tea	5.00
Goblet, 13 oz. Iced Tea ..	5.00	Tumbler, 3 oz.	
Pitcher, 18 oz. Milk	9.00	Footed Wine	5.00
Pitcher, 67 oz.	15.00	Tumbler, 5 oz.	
Plate, 6" Sherbet	1.00	Footed Cordial	3.75
Saucer	1.00	Whiskey, 1½ oz	2.00
Sherbet	2.00		

HOLIDAY, "BUTTON AND BOWS"
(pink, iridescent)
JEANNETTE GLASS COMPANY 1947-1949

	Pink		Pink
Bowl, 5-1/8" Berry	4.25	Pitcher, 6¾", 52 oz.	22.50
Bowl, 7¾" Soup	15.00	Plate, 6" Sherbet	2.00
Bowl, 8½" Large Berry . .	12.00	Plate, 9" Dinner	6.00
Bowl, 9½" Oval		Plate 13¾" Chop	47.50
Vegetable	8.00	Platter, 11-3/8" Oval	7.25
Bowl, 10¾" Console	42.50	Sandwich Tray, 10½" . . .	7.00
Butter Dish and Cover . . .	27.50	Saucer, Two Styles	2.00
Cake Plate, 10½",		Sherbet	4.00
3 Legged	40.00	Sugar	3.50
Candlesticks, 3", Pr.	35.00	Sugar Cover	5.75
Creamer, Footed	4.50	Tumbler, 4", 10 oz. Flat . .	11.00
Cup, Two Sizes	3.50	Tumbler, 4", Footed	20.00
Pitcher, 4¾", 16 oz. Milk	33.00	Tumbler, 6" Footed	39.50

HOMESPUN, "FINE RIB"
(pink, crystal)
JEANNETTE GLASS COMPANY 1939-1940

	Pink or Crystal
Bowl, 4½", Closed Handles	4.00
Bowl, 5" Cereal	7.00
Bowl, 8¼" Large Berry	8.00
Butter Dish and Cover	35.00
Coaster/Ash Tray	3.50
Creamer, Footed	5.50
Cup	3.25
Plate, 6" Sherbet	2.00
Plate, 9¼" Dinner	6.00
Platter, 13" Closed Handles	6.50
Saucer	1.75
Sherbet, Low Flat	5.00
Sugar, Footed	5.50
Tumbler, 4", 9 oz. Water	6.00

	Pink or Crystal
Tumbler, 5¼", 13 oz. Iced Tea	10.00
Tumbler, 4", 5 oz. Footed	6.50
Tumbler, 6¼", 9 oz. Footed	8.00
Tumbler, 6½", 15 oz. Footed	12.00

Homespuns's Child's Tea Set

	Pink or Crystal
Cup	20.00
Saucer	6.00
Plate	8.00
Tea Pot	20.00
Tea Pot Cover	30.00
Set 14 Pieces	185.00

INDIANA CUSTARD,
"FLOWER AND LEAF BAND"
(ivory or custard, early 1930's, white, 1950's)
INDIANA GLASS COMPANY

	Ivory
Bowl, 4-7/8" Berry	4.00
Bowl, 5¾" Cereal.	8.00
Bowl, 7½" Flat Soup	12.00
Bowl, 8¾" Large Berry . .	15.00
Bowl, 9½" Oval Vegetable	17.50
Butter Dish and Cover . . .	45.00
Cup.	15.00
Creamer	10.00

	Ivory
Plate, 5¾" Bread and Butter	3.50
Plate, 7½" Salad	6.00
Plate, 8-7/8" Luncheon . .	7.50
Plate, 9¾" Dinner	10.00
Platter, 11½" Oval.	17.50
Saucer	3.50
Sherbet	50.00
Sugar	6.50
Sugar Cover	9.50

IRIS, "IRIS AND HERRINGBONE" (crystal, iridescent)
(See Reproduction Section, Page 149)
JEANNETTE GLASS COMPANY 1928-1932; 1950; 1970

	Crystal/Iridescent
Bowl, 4½" Berry, Beaded	15.00/4.00
Bowl, 5" Sauce	4.00/4.50
Bowl, 6" Cereal.	15.00/----
Bowl, 7½" Soup	55.00/15.00
Bowl, 8" Large Berry	9.00/8.00
Bowl, 9" Salad.	8.00/7.00
Bowl, 11" Fruit, Ruffled	7.00/7.00
Bowl, 11", Fruit, Straight	20.00/----
Butter Dish and Cover . . .	22.50/27.50
Candlesticks, Pr.	13.00/17.00
Candy Jar and Cover	45.00/----
Coaster	25.00/----
Creamer, Footed	3.50/4.00
Cup	5.50/5.00
Demitasse Cup	12.50/25.00
Demitasse Saucer	17.50/35.00
Goblet, 4" Wine	9.50/12.00

	Crystal/Iridescent
Goblet, 4½" Wine	9.50/----
Goblet, 5¾", 4 oz.	9.00/----
Goblet, 5¾", 8 oz.	11.00/----
Pitcher, 9½" Footed	15.00/18.00
Plate, 5½" Sherbet	4.00/3.50
Plate, 8" Luncheon	24.00/7.50
Plate, 9" Dinner	18.00/11.00
Plate, 11¾" Sandwich . . .	7.50/9.00
Saucer	2.50/3.00
Sherbet, 2½" Footed	7.00/6.00
Sherbet, 4" Footed	7.25/----
Sugar	4.50/4.00
Sugar Cover	5.00/5.00
Tumbler, 4" Flat	23.00/----
Tumbler, 6" Footed	8.00/8.00
Tumbler, 7" Footed	11.00/9.00
Vase, 9".	10.00/10.00

LACE EDGE, "OPEN LACE"
(pink, crystal)
HOCKING GLASS COMPANY 1935-1938

	Pink		Pink
Bowl, 6-3/8" Cereal	6.50	Flower Bowl, Crystal	
Bowl, 7¾" Salad	10.00	Frog	12.00
Bowl, 9½" Plain or		Plate 7¼" Salad	8.50
Ribbed	9.00	Plate, 8¾" Luncheon	7.75
Bowl, 10½" 3 Legs	85.00	Plate, 10½" Dinner	10.50
Butter Dish or Bon Bon		Plate, 10½" Grill	7.50
With Cover	37.50	Plate, 13" 3 Part Solid	
Candlesticks, Pr.	85.00	Lace	15.00
Candy Jar and Cover,		Platter, 13¾"	12.00
Ribbed	20.00	Platter, 13¾", 5 Part	12.00
Compote, 7"	9.50	Relish Dish, 7½" Deep,	
Compote, and Cover,		3 Part	22.50
Footed	17.50	Saucer	5.00
Cookie Jar and Cover . . .	30.00	Sherbet, Footed	30.00
Creamer	9.00	Sugar	9.00
Cup	9.50	Tumbler, 4½", 9 oz.,	
Fish Bowl, 1 gal. 8 oz.		Flat	6.50
(Crystal Only)	12.00	Tumbler, 5", 10½",	
		oz., Footed	25.00
		Vase, 7"	125.00

LAKE COMO
(white with blue decoration)
ANCHOR HOCKING GLASS COMPANY 1934-1937

Bowl, Berry	3.00	Plate, Dinner, 9¼"	3.00
Bowl, Vegetable, 9¾" . . .	6.00	Platter, 11"	7.00
Creamer, Footed	4.00	Salt & Pepper, pr.	15.00
Cup	2.00	Saucer	1.00
Plate, Salad, 7¼"	1.50	Sugar, Footed.	4.00

LAUREL
(French ivory, jade green, white opal and poudre blue)
McKEE GLASS COMPANY 1930's

	Ivory/Green
Bowl, 5" Berry	4.00/5.00
Bowl, 6" Cereal	4.50/5.00
Bowl, 6", Three Legs	7.00/6.00
Bowl, 9", Large Berry....	11.00/8.00
Bowl, 9¾" Oval Vegetable	11.00/13.50
Bowl, 10½", Three Legs .	25.00/25.00
Bowl, 11"	20.00/22.00
Candlesticks, 4" Pr.	22.00/20.00
Cheese Dish and Cover ..	50.00/50.00
Creamer, Short	7.50/7.00
Creamer, Tall	8.00/7.00
Cup	6.00/5.50
Plate, 6" Sherbet	2.50/2.00
Plate, 7½" Salad	5.00/3.00
Plate, 9-1/8" Dinner.....	7.00/5.00
Plate, 9-1/8" Grill.......	6.00/5.00

	Ivory/Green
Platter, 10¾" Oval......	13.00/12.00
Salt and Pepper	50.00/40.00
Saucer	2.50/2.00
Sherbet	7.00/6.00
Sugar, Short	7.50/7.00
Sugar, Tall	8.00/7.00
Tumbler, 4½", 9 oz. Flat .	15.00/----
Tumbler, 5", 12 oz. Flat ..	20.00/----

CHILDREN'S LAUREL TEA SET

	Ivory/Green
Creamer	17.50
Cup	12.50
Plate.................	7.50
Saucer	5.50
Sugar	17.50
14 Piece Set	135.00

LINCOLN INN(amethyst, cobalt, black, red, green, pink, crystal, jade, opaque, green)
FENTON GLASS COMPANY Late 1920's

	Other Blue, Red/Colors		Other Blue, Red/Colors
Ash Tray	9.00/5.00	Nut Dish, Ftd.	10.00/6.00
Bon Bon, Handled, Sq.	10.00/6.00	Plate, 6"	3.50/2.00
Bon Bon, Handled, Oval	10.00/6.00	Plate, 8"	5.50/3.50
Bowl, 5", Fruit	5.00/3.50	Plate, 9¼"	7.50/5.50
Bowl, 6", Cereal	7.00/4.50	Plate, 12"	12.50/8.50
Bowl, 6", Crimped	8.00/5.00	Salt, Pepper, Pr.	125.00/65.00
Bowl, Handled, Olive	8.00/5.00	Saucer	2.50/1.75
Bowl, Finger	6.00/3.75	Sherbet, 4¾"	12.00/7.00
Bowl, 9¼", Ftd.	12.50/10.00	Sugar	10.00/6.00
Bowl, 10½", Ftd.	17.50/12.50	Tumbler, 4 oz., Flat Juice	10.00/6.00
Candy Dish, Ftd., Oval	10.00/6.50	Tumbler, 5 oz., Ftd.	11.00/7.00
Comport	8.00/5.00	Tumbler, 7 oz., Ftd.	12.00/7.50
Creamer	10.00/6.00	Tumbler, 9 oz., Ftd.	12.50/8.50
Cup	5.50/4.00	Tumbler, 12 oz., Ftd.	15.00/10.00
Goblet, Water	15.00/10.00	Vase, 12", Ftd.	45.00/35.00
Goblet, Wine	12.00/8.00		

LORAIN, "BASKET", "NO. 615"
(green, yellow, crystal)
INDIANA GLASS COMPANY 1929-1932

	Green/Yellow
Bowl, 6" Cereal	17.50/30.00
Bowl, 7¼" Salad	20.00/30.00
Bowl, 8" Deep Berry	35.00/45.00
Bowl, 9¾" Oval Vegetable	17.50/25.00
Creamer, Footed	9.50/12.50
Cup	6.00/8.00
Plate, 5½" Sherbet	3.00/4.00
Plate, 7¾" Salad	5.50/6.00
Plate, 8-3/8" Luncheon	7.50/8.00

	Green/Yellow
Plate, 9-3/8" Dinner	12.00/20.00
Plate, 10¼" Dinner	20.00/32.50
Platter, 11½"	15.00/22.00
Relish, 8", 4 Part	10.00/17.50
Saucer	3.00/3.00
Sherbet, Footed	8.00/20.00
Sugar, Footed	9.50/12.50
Tumbler, 4¾", 9 oz. Footed	12.00/13.50

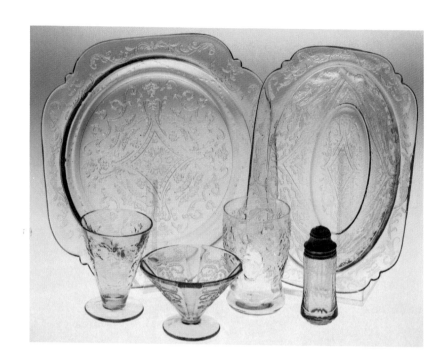

MADRID
(See Reproduction Section, Page 150)
(green, pink, amber, crystal, "Madonna" blue)
FEDERAL GLASS COMPANY 1932-1939

	Amber/Green
Ash Tray, 6" Square	90.00/75.00
Bowl, 4¾" Cream Soup ..	7.00/----
Bowl, 5" Sauce	3.50/5.00
Bowl, 7" Soup	6.50/8.00
Bowl, 8" Salad..........	9.50/12.50
Bowl, 9-3/8" Large Berry .	12.00/15.00
Bowl, 9½", Deep Salad ..	16.50/----
Bowl, 10" Oval Vegetable	9.00/12.00
Bowl, 11" Low Console ..	7.75/----
Butter Dish and Cover ...	50.00/60.00
Candlesticks, 2¼", Pr. ..	12.50/----
Cookie Jar and Cover ...	25.00/----
Creamer, Footed	5.00/7.50
Cup	4.50/5.00
Gravy Boat and Platter ..	7.00/----
Hot Dish Coaster	22.00/25.00
Hot Dish Coaster w/Indent	25.00/27.50
Jam Dish, 7"	12.50/10.50
Jello Mold, 2-1/8" High ..	6.00/----

	Amber/Green
Pitcher, 5½", 36 oz. Juice	22.00/----
Pitcher, 8", 60 oz. Square	25.00/90.00
Pitcher, 8½", 80 oz.	42.50/175.00
Pitcher, 8½", 80 oz. Ice Lip	40.00/175.00
Plate, 6" Sherbet	2.00/3.00
Plate, 7½" Salad	6.50/6.00
Plate, 8-7/8" Luncheon ..	4.00/6.00
Plate, 10½" Dinner	22.00/25.00
Plate, 10½" Grill	7.00/10.00
Plate, 10¼" Relish	7.00/10.00
Plate, 11¼" Cake Round .	8.00/15.00
Platter, 11½" Oval......	7.00/11.00
Salt/Pepper, 3½", Footed	40.00/70.00
Salt/Pepper, 3½", Flat ..	32.50/50.00
Saucer	2.00/2.25
Sherbet, Two Styles	4.50/6.50
Sugar	4.00/6.00
Sugar Cover	19.50/22.50
Tumbler, 3-7/8", 5 oz. ...	10.00/25.00

	Amber/Green
Tumbler, 4¼", 9 oz.	10.00/15.00
Tumbler, 5½", 12 oz.,	
2 Styles	13.50/20.00
Tumbler, 4", 5 oz.	
Footed	13.50/35.00

	Amber/Green
Tumbler, 5½", 10 oz.	
Footed	16.50/25.00
Wooden Lazy Susan,	
7 Hot Dish Coasters . . .	500.00/----

MANHATTAN, "HORIZONTAL RIBBED"
(pink, crystal, green)
ANCHOR HOCKING GLASS COMPANY 1939-1941

	Crystal/Pink		Crystal/Pink
Ashtray, 4"	3.50/----	Relish Tray, 14", 4 Part ..	6.00/8.00
Bowl, 4½" Sauce	4.25/5.00	Relish Tray, 14", 5 Part ..	8.00/12.50
Bowl, 5-3/8" Berry		Pitcher, 42 oz.	12.00/20.00
With Handles	3.00/4.50	Pitcher, 80 oz. Tilted	15.00/27.50
Bowl, 7½" Large Berry ..	4.50/5.00	Plate, 6" Sherbet (Same	
Bowl, 8" Closed Handles .	8.00/9.00	as 6" Plate)	2.00/----
Bowl, 9" Salad..........	6.50/7.00	Plate, 8½" Salad	4.50/5.00
Bowl, 9½" Fruit	12.00/15.00	Plate, 10¼" Dinner	5.00/----
Candlesticks, 4½"		Plate, 14" Sandwich	7.00/8.00
(Double) Pr...........	6.50/----	Salt/Pepper, 2", Pr.	
Candy Dish, 3 Legs	3.00/5.00	(Square).............	10.00/25.00
Candy Dish & Lid	12.50/----	Saucer	2.00/2.00
Coaster, 3½"	2.00/3.00	Sherbet	3.00/4.00
Compote, 5¾"	5.00/7.00	Sugar, Oval	2.50/4.50
Creamer, Oval	2.50/5.00	Tumbler, 10 oz.	
Cup	6.00/ _____	Footed	5.00/6.00
		Vase, 8"	6.00/----

84

MAYFAIR FEDERAL
(crystal, amber, green)
FEDERAL GLASS COMPANY 1934

	Amber/Green
Bowl, 5" Sauce	3.50/5.00
Bowl, 5" Cream Soup	10.00/12.00
Bowl, 6" Cereal.........	10.00/10.00
Bowl, 10" Oval Vegetable	9.00/12.50
Creamer, Footed	6.50/7.50
Cup..................	5.00/6.00

	Amber/Green
Plate, 6¾" Salad	3.50/4.00
Plate, 9½" Dinner	6.00/7.50
Plate, 9½" Grill	6.00/7.50
Platter, 12" Oval........	9.00/12.50
Saucer	2.00/2.00
Sugar, Footed	6.50/7.50
Tumbler, 4½", 9 oz......	10.00/12.50

MAYFAIR, "OPEN ROSE"
(See Reproduction Section Page 145)
(pink, green, blue, yellow, crystal)
HOCKING GLASS COMPANY 1931-1937

	Pink/Blue
Bowl, 5" Cream Soup	25.00/----
Bowl, 5½" Cereal	9.00/13.00
Bowl, 7" Vegetable	12.50/25.00
Bowl, 9", 3-1/8" High, 3 Leg Console	900.00/----
Bowl, 9½", Oval Vegetable	12.00/20.00
Bowl, 10" Vegetable	10.00/20.00
Bowl, 10" Same Covered .	40.00/60.00
Bowl, 11¾" Low Flat	25.00/35.00
Bowl, 12" Deep Scalloped Fruit	25.00/37.50
Butter Dish and Cover or 7" Covered Vegetable	37.50/185.00
Cake Plate, 10" Footed . .	13.50/32.50
Candy Dish and Cover . . .	26.00/90.00
Celery Dish 10" or 10" Divided . . . . ¶	12.00/20.00
Cookie Jar and Lid	21.00/100.00
Creamer, Footed	9.50/37.50
Cup	9.00/22.50

	Pink/Blue
Decanter and Stopper, 32 oz.	67.50/----
Goblet, 4" Cocktail, 3½ oz.	38.50/----
Goblet, 4½" Wine, 3 oz. .	42.50/----
Goblet, 5¾" Water, 9 oz.	23.00/----
Goblet, 7¼" Thin, 9 oz. . .	70.00/65.00
Pitcher, 6", 37 oz.	20.00/57.50
Pitcher, 8", 60 oz.	25.00/65.00
Pitcher, 8½", 80 oz.	40.00/90.00
Plate, 6" (Often Substituted as Saucer) .	5.50/7.00
Plate, 6½" Round Sherbet	6.50/----
Plate, 6½" Round, Off Center Indent	15.00/16.00
Plate, 8½" Luncheon	10.50/16.00
Plate, 9½" Dinner	25.00/27.50
Plate, 9½" Grill	13.50/17.50
Plate, 12" Cake W/Handles	20.00/27.50

	Pink/Blue
Platter, 12" Oval, Open Handles	10.00/18.50
Relish, 8-3/8", 4 part or Non-Partitioned	12.00/25.00
Salt and Pepper, Pr., Flat	29.50/125.00
Salt and Pepper, Pr., Footed	1,500.00/----
Sandwich Server/Center Handle	17.50/32.50
Saucer (Cup Ring)	12.00/----
Saucer (See 6" Plate)	
Sherbet, 2¼" Flat	62.50/45.00
Sherbet, 3" Footed	9.00/----
Sherbet, 4¾" Footed	40.00/35.00
Sugar, Footed	12.00/37.50
Sugar Lid	600.00/----

	Pink/Blue
Tumbler, 3½", 5 oz. Juice	18.50/50.00
Tumbler, 4¼", 9 oz. Water	15.00/42.50
Tumbler, 4¾", 11 oz. Water	37.50/60.00
Tumbler, 5¼", 13½ oz. Iced Tea	22.50/60.00
Tumbler, 3¼", 3 oz. Footed Juice	40.00/----
Tumbler, 5¼", 10 oz. Footed	19.50/50.00
Tumbler, 6½", 15 oz. Footed Iced Tea	21.50/60.00
Vase, (Sweet Pea)	65.00/45.00
Whiskey, 2¼", 1½ oz. . .	52.50/----

MISS AMERICA
(See Reproduction Section Page 152)
(pink, green, crystal, red)
HOCKING GLASS COMPANY 1933-1937

	Crystal/Pink
Bowl, 6¼" Berry	4.00/8.50
Bowl, 8" Curved in at top	22.00/37.50
Bowl, 8¾" Straight Deep Fruit	20.00/33.00
Bowl, 10" Oval Vegetable	7.50/11.00
Butter Dish and Cover	185.00/350.00
Cake Plate, 12" Footed	12.00/20.00
Candy Jar and Cover, 11½"	40.00/72.50
Celery Dish, 10½" Oblong	6.00/9.50
Coaster, 5¾"	10.00/17.50

	Crystal/Pink
Compote, 5"	7.50/12.00
Creamer, Footed	5.50/9.50
Cup	6.00/12.00
Goblet, 3¾", 3 oz. Wine	14.00/37.50
Goblet, 4¾", 5 oz. Juice	16.00/39.00
Goblet, 5½", 10 oz. Water	15.00/27.50
Pitcher, 8", 65 oz. w/Ice Lip	47.00/72.50
Pitcher, 8½", 65 oz. w/Ice Lip	55.00/77.50
Plate, 5¾" Sherbet	2.50/4.00

	Crystal/Pink		Crystal/Pink
Plate, 8½" Salad	4.50/8.50	Saucer	2.00/3.25
Plate, 10½" Dinner	8.00/13.50	Sherbet	6.00/9.00
Plate, 10¼" Grill	6.50/9.50	Sugar	5.00/9.00
Platter, 12" Oval........	9.50/11.00	Tumbler, 4", 5 oz. Juice ..	12.00/28.00
Relish, 8¾", 4 Part......	6.00/9.00	Tumbler, 4½", 10 oz.	
Relish, 11¾" Round		Water	10.00/18.00
Divided	11.00/50.00	Tumbler, 6¾", 14 oz.	
Salt and Pepper, Pr......	20.00/30.00	Iced Tea	18.00/35.00

MODERNTONE, "WEDDING BAND"
(blue, amethyst, platonite fired-on colors)
HAZEL ATLAS GLASS COMPANY 1934-1942

	Cobalt/Amethyst
Ash Tray, 7¾", Match Holder in Center	75.00/----
Bowl, 4¾" Cream Soup	6.50/8.00
Bowl, 5" Berry	7.50/6.00
Bowl, 5" Cream Soup Ruffled	12.00/10.00
Bowl, 6½" Cereal	8.00/8.00
Bowl, 7½" Soup	25.00/20.00
Bowl, 8¾" Large Berry	15.00/13.00
Butter Dish With Metal Cover	50.00/----
Cheese Dish, 7" With Metal Lid	62.50/----
Creamer	4.50/4.50
Cup	4.00/4.00

	Cobalt/Amethyst
Cup (Handle-less) or Custard	7.00/8.00
Plate, 5¾" Sherbet	2.00/2.00
Plate, 6¾" Salad	2.75/3.25
Plate, 7¾" Luncheon	3.50/3.50
Plate, 8-7/8" Dinner	6.00/5.00
Plate, 10½" Sandwich	11.00/8.00
Platter, 11" Oval	11.00/10.00
Platter, 12" Oval	20.00/18.00
Salt and Pepper, Pr.	17.50/23.00
Saucer	1.50/1.50
Sherbet	4.50/4.00
Sugar	4.00/4.00
Sugar Lid in Metal	15.00/15.00
Tumbler, 9 oz.	8.00/----
Whiskey, 1½ oz.	5.00/----

MOONDROPS
(amber, pink, green, cobalt blue, ice blue, red, amethyst, crystal, dark green, light green, jadite, smoke, black)
NEW MARTINSVILLE 1932-1940's

	All Colors		All Colors
Ash Tray	8.50	Butter Dish and Cover . . .	325.00
Bowl, 5¼", Berry	4.00	Candles, 2", Ruffled, Pr. .	17.50
Bowl, 6¾", Soup	8.00	Candles, 4½", Sherbet	
Bowl, 7½", Pickle	9.50	Style, Pr.	17.50
Bowl, 8-3/8" Footed		Candlesticks, 5",	
Concave Top	12.00	"wings,", Pr.	32.50
Bowl, 8½", Three		Candlesticks, 5¼", Triple	
Footed, Divided Relish	9.50	Light, Pr.	35.00
Bowl, 9½" Three Legged,		Candlesticks, 8½", Metal	
Ruffled	12.50	Stem, Pr	20.00
Bowl, 9¾", Oval		Candy Dish, 8", Ruffled . .	12.50
Vegetable	17.50	Cocktail Shaker, with or	
Bowl, 9¾", Covered		without handle, metal	
Casserole	45.00	top	15.00
Bowl, 9¾", Two Handled,		Compote, 4"	7.50
Oval	25.00	Compote, 11½"	16.50
Bowl, 11½", Celery,		Creamer, 2¾", Miniature	8.00
Boat Shaped	17.50	Creamer, 3¾", Regular .	5.50
Bowl, 12", Three Footed,		Cup	6.50
Round Console	22.50	Decanter, Small, 7¾" . . .	27.50
Bowl, 13", Console with		Decanter, Medium, 8½" .	32.50
"wings"	27.50	Decanter, Large, 11¼" . .	37.50

	All Colors		All Colors
Decanter, "rocket", 10¼"	47.50	Plate, 8½" Luncheon	4.50
Goblet, 2-7/8", ¾ oz.		Plate, 9½" Dinner	8.50
Liquor	12.50	Plate, 15" Round	
Goblet, 4", 4 oz. Wine . . .	9.50	Sandwich	13.00
Goblet, 4¼", "rocket"		Plate, 15", Two Handled	
Wine	17.50	Sandwich	22.50
Goblet, 4¾", 5 oz.	8.00	Platter, 12" Oval	12.50
Goblet, 5-1/8", Metal		Saucer	3.00
Stem Wine	8.50	Sherbet, 2-5/8"	6.50
Goblet, 5½", Metal Stem		Sherbet, 4½"	8.50
Wine	8.50	Sugar, 2¾"	8.00
Goblet, 6¼", Water,		Sugar, 4"	6.50
9 oz.	13.50	Tumbler, 2¾", Shot, 2 oz.	6.50
Mug, 5-1/8", 12 oz.	12.50	Tumbler, 2¾", Handled	
Perfume Bottle, "rocket"	25.00	Shot, 2 oz.	7.50
Pitcher, Small, 6-7/8",		Tumbler, 3¾", Footed	
22 oz.	77.50	Juice, 3 oz.	7.50
Pitcher, Medium, 8-1/8",		Tumbler, 3-5/8", 5 oz. . . .	6.00
32 oz.	115.00	Tumbler, 4-3/8", 7 oz. . . .	7.50
Pitcher, Large With Lip,		Tumbler, 4-3/8", 8 oz. . . .	8.50
8", 50 oz.	125.00	Tumbler, 4-7/8",	
Pitcher, Large, No Lip,		Handled, 9 oz.	9.50
8-1/8", 53 oz.	125.00	Tumbler, 4-7/8", 9 oz. . . .	10.00
Plate, 5-7/8", Bread		Tumbler, 5-1/8", 12 oz. . .	10.50
and Butter	2.50	Tray, 7½", For	
Plate, 6-1/8", Sherbet . . .	2.50	Miniature	
Plate, 6" Round, Off-		Sugar/Creamer	15.00
Center Indent for		Vase, 7¾", Flat, Ruffled	
Sherbet	4.00	Top	32.50
Plate, 7-1/8", Salad	4.00	Vase, 9¼", "rocket" style	52.50

MOONSTONE
(crystal with opalescent hobnails)
ANCHOR HOCKING GLASS COMPANY 1941-1946

	Opalescent		Opalescent
Bowl, 5½" Berry	6.25	Cup	4.50
Bowl, 5½" Crimped		Goblet, 10 oz.	9.75
Dessert	4.50	Heart Bonbon, One	
Bowl, 6½" Crimped,		Handle	6.00
Handled	6.00	Plate, 6¼" Sherbet	2.25
Bowl, 7¾" Flat	7.50	Plate, 8" Luncheon	5.00
Bowl, 7¾" Divided Relish	6.50	Plate, 10" Sandwich	10.00
Bowl, 9½" Crimped	9.00	Puff Box and Cover,	
Bowl, Cloverleaf	7.50	4¾", Round	11.50
Candleholder, Pr.	12.50	Saucer (Same as Sherbet	
Candy Jar and Cover, 6"	12.50	Plate)	2.25
Cigarette Jar and Cover	11.50	Sherbet, Footed	5.50
Cologne Bottle	7.50	Sugar, Footed	4.00
Creamer	5.00	Vase, 5½" Bud	8.50

MT. PLEASANT, "DOUBLE SHIELD"
(black, cobalt blue, green, pink)
L.E. SMITH COMPANY 1920's-1934

	Cobalt/Black		Cobalt/Black
Bon Bon, Rolled Up Handles	14.50/7.50	Cup (Waffle-like Crystal)	3.00/-----
Bowl, 3 Footed, Rolled-In Edges, As Rose Bowl	8.00/9.00	Cup	6.00/5.00
Bowl, 8" Scalloped, Two Handles	14.00/13.00	Plate, 8" Scalloped or Square	6.00/8.00
Bowl, 8" Two Handled Square	8.00/9.00	Plate, 8" Solid Handles	7.00/8.00
Candlesticks, Single Stem, Pr.	15.00/12.00	Plate, 10½" Cake with Solid Handles	12.00/18.00
Candlesticks, Double Stem, Pr.	25.00/18.00	Salt and Pepper Shakers (Two Styles)	20.00/18.00
Creamer (Waffle-like Crystal)	4.00/-----	Saucer, Square or Scalloped	2.00/2.00
Creamer (Scalloped Edges)	7.00/7.00	Sherbet, Scalloped Edges	7.00/9.00
		Sugar (Waffle-like Crystal)	4.00/-----
		Sugar (Scalloped Edges)	7.00/7.00

NEW CENTURY, and incorrectly, "LYDIA RAY"
(pink, green, crystal, amethyst, cobalt)
HAZEL ATLAS GLASS COMPANY 1930-1935

	Green		Green
Ash Tray/Coaster, 5-3/8"	22.00	Plate, 8½" Salad	5.50
Bowl, 4½" Berry........	4.00	Plate, 10" Dinner	8.00
Bowl, 4¾" Cream Soup ..	7.50	Plate, 10" Grill	7.00
Bowl, 8" Large Berry	9.00	Platter, 11" Oval........	9.00
Bowl, 9" Covered		Salt and Pepper, Pr......	21.50
Casserole	40.00	Saucer	1.50
Butter Dish and Cover ...	42.50	Sherbet, 3"	5.00
Cup..................	4.50	Sugar	3.50
Creamer	5.00	Sugar Cover	8.00
Decanter and Stopper ...	35.00	Tumbler, 3½", 5 oz......	7.00
Goblet, 2½ oz. Wine	10.00	Tumbler, 4-1/8", 9 oz. ...	7.50
Goblet, 3¼ oz. Cocktail .	12.00	Tumbler, 5", 10 oz.......	9.00
Pitcher, 7¾", 60 oz., with		Tumbler, 5¼", 12 oz.....	12.50
or without Ice Lip	20.00	Tumbler, 4", 5 oz. Footed	8.00
Pitcher, 8", 80 oz., with		Tumbler, 4-7/8", 9 oz.	
or without Ice Lip	25.00	Footed	10.00
Plate, 6" Sherbet	2.25	Whiskey, 2½", 1½ oz. ..	5.00
Plate, 7-1/8" Breakfast ..	5.00		

NEWPORT, "HAIRPIN"
(cobalt blue, amethyst, "Platonite" white and fired on colors)
Hazel Atlas Glass Company 1936-1940

	Cobalt/ Amethyst		Cobalt/ Amethyst
Bowl, 4¼" Berry	2.50/3.50	Plate, 11½" Sandwich	11.00/13.00
Bowl, 4¾" Cream Soup	6.00/6.50	Platter, 11¾" Oval	12.00/14.00
Bowl, 5¼" Cereal	4.00/4.50	Salt and Pepper	25.00/30.00
Bowl, 8¼" Large Berry	8.00/11.00	Saucer	2.00/2.00
Cup	4.00/3.50	Sherbet	5.00/5.00
Creamer	5.50/4.50	Sugar	5.50/5.00
Plate, 6" Sherbet	2.00/2.00	Tumbler, 4½", 9 oz.	10.00/8.00
Plate, 8½" Luncheon	4.00/5.00		

NORMANDIE, "BOUQUET AND LATTICE"
(iridescent, amber, pink)
FEDERAL GLASS COMPANY 1933-1940

	Amber/Pink		Amber/Pink
Bowl, 5" Berry	3.50/4.00	Platter, 11¾"	8.00/10.00
Bowl, 6½" Cereal	6.00/7.00	Salt and Pepper, Pr.	30.00/35.00
Bowl, 8½" Large Berry	7.00/9.00	Saucer	1.50/2.50
Bowl, 10" Oval Veg.	8.00/15.00	Sherbet	4.00/5.00
Creamer, Footed	4.50/5.00	Sugar	3.00/3.00
Cup	4.00/4.00	Sugar Lid	55.00/85.00
Pitcher, 8", 80 oz.	40.00/60.00	Tumbler, 4", 5 oz.	
Plate, 6" Sherbet	2.00/2.00	Juice	10.00/20.00
Plate, 8" Salad	5.00/6.00	Tumbler, 4¼", 9 oz.	
Plate, 9¼" Luncheon	4.00/7.50	Water	9.00/15.00
Plate, 11" Dinner	10.00/25.00	Tumbler, 5", 12 oz.	
Plate, 11" Grill	7.50/8.50	Iced Tea	13.00/22.00

NO. 610, "PYRMAMID"
(green, pink, yellow, crystal) (Black, 1974-75 by Tiara)
INDIANA GLASS COMPANY 1928-1932

	Pink/Yellow
Bowl, 4¾" Berry	4.50/12.50
Bowl, 8½" Master Berry	10.00/25.00
Bowl, 9½" Oval	20.00/30.00
Bowl, 9½" Pickle	20.00/30.00
Creamer	8.00/13.00
Ice Tub	25.00/150.00
Ice Tub and Lid	30.00/75.00
Pitcher	95.00/75.00

	Pink/Yellow
Relish Tray, 4 Part, Handled	20.00/30.00
Sugar	8.00/13.00
Tray for Creamer and Sugar	10.00/18.00
Tumbler, 8 oz., Footed	12.00/25.00
Tumbler, 11 oz., Footed	20.00/35.00

NO. 612, "HORSESHOE"
(green, yellow, crystal)
INDIANA GLASS COMPANY 1930-1933

	Green/Yellow
Bowl, 4½" Berry	16.00/12.00
Bowl, 6½" Cereal	10.00/12.00
Bowl, 7½" Salad	12.00/13.00
Bowl, 8½" Vegetable	15.00/18.00
Bowl, 9½" Large Berry	20.00/23.00
Bowl, 10½" Oval Vegetable	12.00/14.50
Butter Dish and Cover	475.00/-----
Candy in Metal Holder Motif on Lid Only	100.00/-----
Creamer, Footed	9.00/9.50
Cup	5.50/6.00
Pitcher, 8½", 64 oz.	175.00/190.00
Plate, 6" Sherbet	2.50/4.00

	Green/Yellow
Plate, 8-3/8" Salad	4.00/5.50
Plate, 9-3/8" Luncheon	6.00/7.00
Plate, 10-3/8" Dinner	12.00/13.00
Plate, 10-3/8" Grill	15.00/15.00
Plate, 11¼" Sandwich	8.00/10.00
Platter, 10¾" Oval	12.00/13.00
Relish, 3 Part, Footed	10.00/12.00
Saucer	3.00/3.00
Sherbet	8.00/9.75
Sugar, Open	8.00/8.50
Tumbler, 4¼", 9 oz.	45.00/-----
Tumbler, 4¾", 12 oz.	70.00/-----
Tumbler, 9 oz., Footed	10.00/12.00
Tumbler, 12 oz., Footed	50.00/60.00

NO. 616, "VERNON"
(green, crystal, yellow)
INDIANA GLASS COMPANY 1930-1932

	Green/Yellow		Green/Yellow
Creamer, Footed	19.00/17.00	Saucer	3.50/3.00
Cup	13.00/11.00	Sugar, Footed	19.00/17.00
Plate, 8" Luncheon	6.50/7.00	Tumbler, 5", Footed	23.00/20.00
Plate, 11" Sandwich	20.00/18.00		

NO. 618, "PINEAPPLE & FLORAL"
(crystal, amber, fired-on red)
INDIANA GLASS COMPANY 1932-1937

	Crystal/Amber		Crystal/Amber
Ash Tray, 4½"	12.50/-----	Plate, 9-3/8" Dinner	6.00/8.00
Bowl, 6" Cereal	14.00/15.00	Plate, 11½" Sandwich . . .	8.00/9.50
Bowl, 7" Salad	4.00/8.00	Platter, 11" Closed	
Bowl, 10" Oval		Handles	8.00/10.00
Vegetable	12.00/15.00	Platter, Relish, 11½",	
Compote, Diamond		Divided	12.00/8.00
Shaped	1.00/6.00	Saucer	2.00/2.50
Creamer		Sherbet, Footed	9.00/10.00
Diamond Shaped	6.00/7.50	Sugar, Diamond Shaped .	6.00/7.50
Cream Soup	12.50/15.00	Tumbler, 4¼", 8 oz.	14.00/18.00
Cup	5.00/6.00	Tumbler, 4½", 10 oz.	18.00/20.00
Plate, 6" Sherbet	2.00/3.00	Vase, Cone Shaped,	
Plate, 8-3/8" Salad	3.50/4.00	Large	20.00/-----

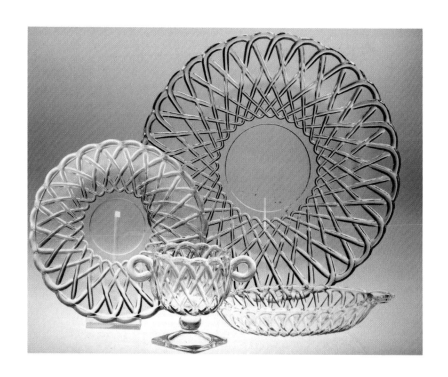

NO. 622 "PRETZEL"
(crystal)
INDIANA GLASS COMPANY 1930's

	Crystal
Bowl, 4½" Fruit Cup	1.50
Bowl, 7" Olive, Leaf Shaped.............	2.25
Bowl, 7½" Soup	2.50
Bowl, 8½", 2 Handled, Pickle	2.50
Bowl, 9-3/8" Berry	3.50
Bowl, 10¼" Celery......	4.00
Creamer	3.00
Cup	1.75

	Crystal
Pitcher, 39 oz...........	15.00
Plate, 6" Bread & Butter .	1.25
Plate, 6" Tab Handled ...	1.50
Plate, 8-3/8" Salad	1.75
Plate, 9-3/8" Dinner.....	2.50
Plate, 11½" Sandwich ...	3.50
Saucer	.50
Sugar	2.75
Tumbler, 5 oz., Juice	2.50
Tumbler, 9 oz., Water ...	3.25

OLD CAFE
(pink, crystal, ruby red)
HOCKING GLASS COMPANY 1936-1938; 1940

	Pink/Red		Pink/Red
Bowl, 3¾" Berry	1.50/3.50	Olive Dish, 6" Oblong	3.00/-----
Bowl, 5", One or Two Handles	2.50/-----	Plate, 6" Sherbet	1.00/-----
Bowl, 5½" Cereal	3.50/6.00	Plate, 10" Dinner	9.00/-----
Bowl, 9", Closed Handles	7.00/-----	Saucer	2.00/-----
Candy Dish, 8" Low	3.00/6.00	Sherbet, Low Footed	3.00/5.00
Cup	3.00/5.00	Tumbler, 3" Juice	3.00/5.00
Lamp	8.50/12.00	Tumbler, 4" Water	4.00/7.00
		Vase, 7¼"	7.50/12.00

OLD ENGLISH, "THREADING"
(green, pink, amber)
INDIANA GLASS COMPANY Late 1920's

	All Colors		All Colors
Bowl, 4" Berry	8.50	Plate, Indent for	
Bowl, 9" Footed Fruit	17.50	Compote	15.00
Bowl, 9½" Flat	20.00	Sandwich Server,	
Candlesticks, 4", Pr.	17.50	Center Handle	20.00
Candy Jar with Lid, Ftd.	30.00	Sherbet	12.00
Candy and Lid, Flat	30.00	Sugar	7.00
Compote, 3½" Tall, 7"		Sugar Cover	14.00
Across	10.00	Tumbler, 4½" Footed	9.00
Creamer	9.00	Tumbler, 5½" Footed	15.00
Fruit Stand, 11" Footed	20.00	Vase, 13"	25.00
Goblet, 5¾", 8 oz.	13.00		

OVIDE, incorrectly dubbed "New Century"
(green, white , black)
HAZEL ATLAS GLASS COMPANY 1930-1935

	Green/Black		Green/Black
Bowl, 4¾" Berry	-----/6.50	Plate, 6" Sherbet	1.00/2.50
Bowl, 5½" Cereal	-----/6.50	Plate, 8" Luncheon	1.50/5.00
Bowl, 8" Large Berry	-----/13.50	Salt and Pepper, Pr.	7.50/17.50
Candy Dish and Cover	12.00/20.00	Saucer	1.25/3.00
Cocktail, Fruit, Footed	1.50/6.00	Sherbet	1.50/6.50
Creamer	2.50/7.50	Sugar, Open	2.50/7.50
Cup	1.50/5.00		

OYSTER AND PEARL
(pink, crystal, ruby red, white with fired on pink or green)
ANCHOR HOCKING GLASS 1938-1940

	Pink/Red		Pink/Red
Bowl, 5¼" Round or Handled	3.00/7.50	Bowl, 6½" Deep, Handled	6.50/9.50
Bowl, 5¼" Heart Shaped, One Handled	3.50/-----	Bowl, 10½" Fruit, Deep	10.00/25.00
		Candleholder, 3½", Pr.	12.00/25.00
		Plate, 13½" Sandwich	7.00/22.50
		Relish Dish, 10¼" Oblong	5.00/-----

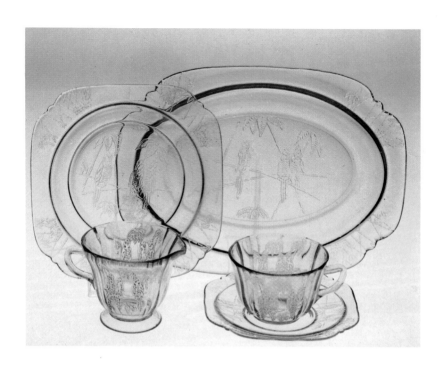

"PARROT", SYLVAN
(green, amber, crystal)
FEDERAL GLASS COMPANY 1931-1932

	Green/Amber
Bowl, 5" Berry	9.00/8.00
Bowl, 7" Soup	16.00/20.00
Bowl, 8" Large Berry	40.00/45.00
Bowl, 10" Oval Vegetable	20.00/25.00
Butter Dish and Cover	200.00/500.00
Creamer, Footed	12.00/15.00
Cup	13.00/15.00
Hot Plate, 5"	175.00/-----
Jam Dish, 7"	20.00/20.00
Pitcher, 8½", 80 oz.	500.00/-----
Plate, 5¾" Sherbet	7.50/8.00
Plate, 7½" Salad	10.00/-----
Plate, 9" Dinner	15.00/17.50
Plate, 10½" Grill, Round	10.00/-----

	Green/Amber
Plate, 10½" Grill, Square	-----/10.00
Plate, 10¼" Square	15.00/17.50
Platter, 11¼" Oblong	20.00/35.00
Salt and Pepper, Pr.	140.00/-----
Saucer	5.00/5.00
Sherbet, Footed, Cone	10.00/9.00
Sherbet, 4¼" High	100.00/-----
Sugar	11.00/12.00
Sugar Cover	40.00/100.00
Tumbler, 4¼", 10 oz.	45.00/-----
Tumbler, 5½", 12 oz.	60.00/75.00
Tumbler, 5¾" Footed, Heavy	50.00/65.00

PATRICIAN, "SPOKE"
(pink, green, amber, crystal)
FEDERAL GLASS COMPANY 1933-1937

	Amber/Green
Bowl, 4¾", Cream Soup .	8.00/7.50
Bowl, 5" Berry	5.50/5.25
Bowl, 6" Cereal	12.00/10.00
Bowl, 8½" Large Berry . .	20.00/12.50
Bowl, 12" Oval	
Vegetable	13.00/10.00
Butter Dish and Cover . . .	48.00/75.00
Cookie Jar and Cover . . .	40.00/175.00
Creamer, Footed	5.00/6.25
Cup	5.00/5.00
Pitcher, 8", 75 oz.	55.00/75.00
Pitcher, 8¼", 75 oz.	55.00/75.00
Plate, 6" Sherbet	5.00/2.75
Plate, 7½" Salad	7.00/6.00

	Amber/Green
Plate, 9" Luncheon	5.00/5.00
Plate, 10½" Dinner	4.00/15.00
Plate, 10½" Grill	5.00/8.50
Platter, 11½" Oval	8.00/12.00
Salt and Pepper, Pr.	30.00/42.50
Saucer	3.50/3.25
Sherbet	5.25/7.75
Sugar	3.50/5.00
Sugar Cover	22.00/35.00
Tumbler, 4", 5 oz.	15.00/15.00
Tumbler, 4½", 9 oz.	13.00/14.00
Tumbler, 5½", 14 oz.	20.00/22.00
Tumbler, 5½", 8 oz.	
Footed	25.00/35.00

PETALWARE
(pink, crystal, monax, cremax)
MACBETH EVANS GLASS COMPANY 1930-1940

	Pink/Monax		Pink/Monax
Bowl, 4½" Cream Soup ..	4.00/5.00	Plate, 6" Sherbet	1.25/2.00
Bowl, 5¾" Cereal	3.00/4.00	Plate, 8" Salad	1.50/3.00
Bowl, 8¾" Large Berry ..	7.00/8.50	Plate, 9" Dinner	3.00/4.00
Cup..................	2.50/3.50	Plate, 11" Salver........	3.50/6.00
Creamer, Footed	3.00/3.75	Platter, 13" Oval........	4.00/6.00
Lamp Shade (Many Sizes)	-----/7.50	Saucer	1.25/1.25
Mustard with Metal Cover in Cobalt Blue Only	6.00	Sherbet, Low Footed	3.00/4.50
		Sugar, Footed	3.00/3.75

PRINCESS
(green, pink, topaz, apricot)
HOCKING GLASS COMPANY 1931-1935

	Pink/Green		Pink/Green
Ash Tray, 4½"	55.00/45.00	Plate, 8" Salad	5.00/6.50
Bowl, 4½" Berry	7.00/12.00	Plate, 9½" Dinner	7.00/13.50
Bowl, 5" Cereal or		Plate, 9½" Grill	4.50/5.50
Oatmeal	13.00/14.00	Plate, 11½", Grill,	
Bowl, 9" Salad		Closed Handles	4.50/6.00
Octagonal	15.00/17.00	Plate, 11½", Sandwich,	
Bowl, 9½" Hat Shaped . .	12.00/17.00	Handled	7.50/8.50
Bowl, 10" Oval		Platter, 12" Closed	
Vegetable	9.50/11.00	Handles	9.50/10.00
Butter Dish and Cover . . .	60.00/65.00	Relish, 7½", Divided	10.00/12.00
Cake Stand, 10"	8.50/10.00	Relish, 7½", Plain	-----/45.00
Candy Dish and Cover . . .	25.00/27.50	Salt and Pepper, Pr., 4½"	23.00/32.50
Coaster	12.00/15.00	Saucer (Same as Sherbet	
Cookie Jar and Cover . . .	25.00/27.00	Plate)	2.00/3.50
Creamer, Oval	7.50/5.50	Sherbet, Footed	8.00/11.00
Cup	3.50/5.50	Sugar	3.50/5.00
Pitcher, 6", 37 oz.	18.00/22.50	Sugar Cover . .	7.00/9.00
Pitcher, 7-3/8", 24 oz.		Tumbler, 3", 5 oz. Juice . .	12.00/14.00
Footed	300.00/400.00	Tumbler, 4", 9 oz. Water .	10.00/15.00
Pitcher, 8", 60 oz.	25.00/30.00	Tumbler, 5¼", 12 oz. Iced	
Plate, 5½", Sherbet	2.00/3.50	Tea	12.50/20.00

	Pink/Green		Pink/Green
Tumbler, 4¾", 9 oz.		Tumbler, 6½", Footed,	
Sq. Ft.	35.00/40.00	12½ oz.	20.00/36.00
Tumbler, 5¼", 10 oz.		Vase, 8"	13.00/15.00
Footed	12.00/16.00		

QUEEN MARY, "VERTICAL RIBBED" (pink, crystal)
HOCKING GLASS COMPANY 1936-1940

	Crystal or Pink		Crystal or Pink
Ash Tray, Oval, 2"x3¾" .	2.00	Square	4.00
Bowl, 4", One Handle or		Compote, 5¾"	3.00
None	2.50	Creamer, Oval	3.50
Bowl, 5" Berry, 6" Cereal	3.00	Cup	4.00
Bowl, 5½", Two Handles	3.00	Plate, 6" and 6-5/8"	2.00
Bowl, 8¾" Large Berry . .	5.00	Plate, 8½" Salad	3.50
* Butter Dish or Preserve		** Plate, 9¾" Dinner	4.00
and Cover	22.50	Plate, 12" Sandwich	5.00
Candy Dish and Cover . . .	15.00	Plate, 14" Serving Tray . .	7.00
Candlesticks, 4½",		Relish Tray, 12", 3 Part . .	8.00
Double Branch, Pr.	9.50	Relish Tray, 14", 4 Part . .	8.00
Candlesticks, Ruby Red		Salt and Pepper, Pr.	10.00
Pr.	25.00	Saucer	1.00
Celery or Pickle Dish,		Sherbet, Footed	3.50
5"x10"	3.00	Sugar, Oval	3.00
Cigarette Jar, Oval,		Tumbler, 3½", 5 oz. Juice	2.50
2"x3"	4.50	Tumbler, 4", 9 oz. Water .	4.00
Coaster, 3½"	2.00	Tumbler, 5", 10 oz.	
Coaster/Ash Tray, 4¼"		Footed	12.00

*Pink — $75.00
**Pink — $10.00

RADIANCE
(Red, cobalt and ice blue, amber, crystal)
NEW MARTINSVILLE 1936-1939

	Red/Other Colors		Red/Other Colors
Bon Bon, 6"	7.50/5.50	Creamer	9.00/6.50
Bon Bon, 6", Ftd........	9.00/6.00	Cruet, Individual	25.00/20.00
Bon Bon, 6", Covered....	20.00/13.50	Cup	6.50/4.50
Bowl, 5", 2 Handled, Nut.	9.50/6.50	Decanter, Handled	
Bowl, 7", 2 Part.........	12.50/7.50	With Stopper	75.00/50.00
Bowl, 7", Pickle	9.00/6.00	Lamp, 12"	70.00/35.00
Bowl, 8", 3 Part Relish ...	15.00/9.00	Mayonnaise, 3 Pc. Set ...	17.50/10.00
Bowl, 10", Celery	11.00/7.50	Pitcher, 64 Oz.	150.00/100.00
Bowl, 10", Crimped	15.50/10.00	Plate, 8" Luncheon	6.00/4.00
Bowl, 10", Flared	15.00/9.75	Plate, 14", Punch Bowl	
Bowl, 12", Crimped	22.50/12.50	Liner	30.00/15.00
Bowl, 12", Flared	22.00/12.00	Punch Bowl	75.00/35.00
Butter Dish	300.00/145.00	Punch Cup	6.00/4.00
Candlestick, 8", Pr.	25.00/15.00	Punch Ladle...........	75.00/40.00
Candle, 2 Light, Pr.	37.50/22.50	Salt & Pepper, Pr.	30.00/20.00
Cheese and Cracker, 11		Saucer	2.50/2.00
Plate Set	2..00/13.50	Sugar	9.50/6.50
Comport, 5"............	9.00/6.00	Tray, Oval	20.00/15.00
Comport, 6"............	10.00/7.00	Tumbler, 9 Oz.	12.50/8.50
Condiment Set, 4 Pc.		Vase, 10", Flared	20.00/10.00
On Tray	125.00/85.00	Vase, 12", Crimped	30.00/15.00

RAINDROPS, "OPTIC DESIGN"
(green, crystal)
FEDERAL GLASS COMPANY 1929-1933

	Green		Green
Bowl, 4½" Fruit	2.00	Saucer	1.00
Bowl, 6" Cereal	3.00	Sherbet	3.50
Cup	3.00	Sugar	3.00
Creamer	4.50	Sugar Cover	20.00
Plate, 6" Sherbet	1.50	Tumbler, 3", 4 oz.	3.00
Plate, 8" Luncheon	2.50	Whiskey, 1-7/8"	3.00
Salt and Pepper, Pr.	40.00		

RIBBON
(green, black, crystal)
HAZEL ATLAS GLASS COMPANY 1930-1932

	Green/Black
Bowl, 4" Berry	2.00/-----
Bowl, 8" Large Berry	10.00/15.00
Candy Dish and Cover . . .	22.00/-----
Creamer, Footed	3.50/9.00
Cup	3.25/-----
Plate, 6¼" Sherbet	1.25/-----

	Green/Black
Plate, 8"	
Luncheon	2.50/8.00
Salt and Pepper, Pr.	12.00/25.00
Saucer	1.50/-----
Sherbet, Footed	3.00/-----
Sugar, Footed	3.50/19.00
Tumbler, 5½", 10 oz.	8.00/-----
Tumbler, 6½", 13 oz.	10.00/-----

RING, "BANDED RINGS"
(crystal, green and crystal w/decoration)
HOCKING GLASS COMPANY 1927-1932

	Crystal/Dec.
Bowl, 5" Berry	1.75/2.25
Bowl, 8" Large Berry	3.00/5.00
Butter Tub or Ice Bucket	8.00/12.50
Cocktail Shaker	7.00/10.00
Cup	2.50/3.00
Creamer, Footed	2.50/3.50
Decanter and Stopper	12.00/15.00
Goblet, 7" to 8" (Varies) 9 oz.	4.00/6.00
Pitcher, 8", 60 oz.	8.00/12.00
Pitcher, 8½", 80 oz.	10.00/15.00
Plate, 6¼" Sherbet	1.25/1.00
Plate, 6", Off Center Ring	1.50/2.00
Plate, 8" Luncheon	1.50/2.50
Salt and Pepper, Pr., 3"	12.00/20.00

	Crystal/Dec.
Sandwich Server Center Handle	9.00/15.00
Saucer	1.00/1.50
Sherbet, Low (for 6½" Plate)	3.50/4.50
Sherbet, 4¾" Footed	4.00/5.50
Sugar, Footed	2.50/3.50
Tumbler, 3½", 5 oz.	2.00/3.50
Tumbler, 4¼", 9 oz	2.50/3.00
Tumbler, 5-1/8", 12 oz.	3.00/4.00
Tumbler, 3½", Footed, Cocktail	3.00/4.00
Tumbler, 5½", Footed, Water	3.00/4.00
Tumbler, 6½", Footed, Iced Tea	4.00/7.50
Whiskey, 2", 1½ oz.	2.50/4.50

ROCK CRYSTAL,
"EARLY AMERICAN ROCK CRYSTAL"
(pink, green, cobalt, red, yellow, amber, blue-green, crystal)
McKEE GLASS COMPANY 1920's and 1930's in color

	Crystal/Pink
*Bon Bon, 7½", S.E.	6.00/12.00
Bowl, 4", 5" Fruit, S.E.	3.00/5.00
**Bowl, 5" Finger Bowl with 7" Plate, P.E.	8.00/12.00
Bowl, 7" Pickle or Spoon Tray	8.00/14.00
Bowl, 7", 8" Salad, S.E.	6.50/9.00
Bowl, 9", 10½" Salad, S.E.	10.00/15.00
Bowl, 11½" Two Part Relish	9.00/15.00
Bowl, 12" Oblong Celery	7.00/12.00
Bowl, 12½" Footed Center Bowl	12.00/18.00
Bowl, 13" Roll Tray	15.00/20.00
Bowl, 14" Six Part Relish	15.00/30.00
Candelabra, Two Lite	15.00/20.00
Candelabra, Three Lite	17.00/25.00
Candlesticks, 5½" Low, Pr.	12.00/18.00

	Crystal/Pink
Candlesticks, 8½" Tall, Pr.	40.00/50.00
Candy and Cover, Round	15.00/35.00
Cake Stand, 11" Footed, 2¾" High	12.00/25.00
Compote, 7"	9.00/25.00
Creamer, 9 oz., Footed	10.00/15.00
Cruet and Stopper, 6 oz. Oil	35.00/50.00
Cup, 7 oz.	7.00/10.00
Goblet, 7½" oz., 8 oz. Low Footed	9.00/16.00
Goblet, 11 oz., Low Footed, Iced Tea	10.00/18.00
Jelly, 5" Footed, S.E.	9.00/12.00
Lamp, Electric	40.00/80.00
Parfait, 3½ oz., Low Foot	5.00/-----
Pitcher, ½ Gal., 7½" High	50.00/95.00

117

	Crystal/Pink
Pitcher Large	60.00/100.00
Plate, 6" Bread and Butter, S.E.	2.50/3.50
Plate, 7½", 8½" Salad, P.E. & S.E.	3.00/5.00
Plate, 9", 10½", 11½" Cake, S.E. (small center design)	8.00/15.00
Plate, 10½" Dinner, S.E. (large center design)	10.00/15.00
Salt and Pepper 2 styles	35.00/50.00
Salt Dip	20.00/-----
Sandwich Server Center Handled	15.00/25.00
Saucer	3.00/4.00
Sherbet or Egg, 3½ oz., Footed	8.00/12.00
Stemware, 1 oz., Footed Cordial	10.00/15.00
Stemware, 2 oz., 3 oz., Footed Wines	8.00/15.00
Stemware, 3½ oz., Footed Cocktail	7.00/12.00

	Crystal/Pink
Stemware, 6 oz., Footed Champagne	8.00/13.00
Stemware, 8 oz., Large Footed Goblet	10.00/15.00
Sundae, 6 oz. Low Footed	7.00/12.00
Sugar, 10 oz. Open	7.00/12.00
Sugar, 10 oz., Covered	20.00/35.00
Tumbler, 2½" oz., Whiskey	6.00/12.00
Tumbler, 5 oz. Juice	8.00/12.00
Tumbler, 5 oz., Old Fashioned	9.00/12.00
Tumbler, 9 oz., Concave or Straight	9.00/12.00
Tumbler, 12 oz., Concave or Straight	12.00/15.00
Vase, 11" Footed	20.00/35.00

*S.E. McKee designation for scalloped edge
**P.E. McKee designation for plain edge

ROSE CAMEO
(green)
BELMONT TUMBLER COMPANY 1931

	Green		Green
Bowl, 4 ½" Berry	2.50	Sherbet	3.00
Bowl, 5" Cereal.........	4.00	Tumbler, 5", Footed	
Plate, 7" Salad	3.25	(2 Styles)	7.00

ROSEMARY, "DUTCH ROSE"
(pink, green, amber)
FEDERAL GLASS COMPANY 1935-1937

	Amber/Green		Amber/Green
Bowl, 5" Berry	3.00/4.50	Plate, 6¾" Salad	3.00/5.00
Bowl, 5" Cream Soup	6.00/10.00	Plate, Dinner	5.00/9.00
Bowl, 6" Cereal	10.00/10.00	Plate, Grill	4.00/8.00
Bowl, 10" Oval		Platter, 12" Oval	7.00/10.00
Vegetable	7.00/10.00	Saucer	1.50/2.00
Creamer, Footed	6.00/7.50	Sugar, Footed	6.00/7.50
Cup	3.00/6.00	Tumbler, 4¼, 9 oz.	9.00/12.50

ROULETTE, "MANY WINDOWS"
(pink, green)
HOCKING GLASS COMPANY 1935-1939

	Pink/Green		Pink/Green
Bowl, 9" Fruit	6.00/7.50	Tumbler, 3¼", 7½ oz.	
Cup	2.50/3.25	Old Fashioned	5.00/5.50
Pitcher, 8", 64 oz.	15.00/19.00	Tumbler, 4-1/8", 9 oz.	
Plate, 6" Sherbet	1.25/1.50	Water	5.00/9.00
Plate, 8½" Luncheon	3.00/3.25	Tumbler, 5-1/8", 12 oz.	
Plate, 12" Sandwich	4.00/6.50	Iced Tea	7.00/9.00
Saucer	1.00/1.50	Tumbler, 5½", 10 oz.	
Sherbet	3.00/3.00	Footed	8.00/8.50
Tumbler, 3¼", 5 oz. Juice	3.00/3.75	Whiskey, 2½", 1½ oz. ..	4.00/6.50

"ROUND ROBIN"
(green, iridescent)
1927-1932

	Green/Irides-cent		Green/Irrides-cent
Bowl, 4" Berry	3.00/3.50	Plate, 8" Luncheon	2.00/3.00
Cup, Footed	3.00/3.50	Plate, 12" Sandwich	3.50/4.00
Creamer, Footed	4.00/5.00	Saucer	1.25/1.50
Domino Tray	15.00/-----	Sherbet	2.50/3.50
Plate, 6" Sherbet	1.25/1.50	Sugar	4.00/5.00

ROXANA
(yellow, white, crystal)
HAZEL ATLAS GLASS COMPANY 1932

	Yellow		Yellow
Bowl, 4½"x2-3/8"	4.50	Saucer	2.00
Bowl, 5" Berry	3.00	Sherbet, Footed	3.00
Bowl, 6" Cereal.........	5.00	Tumbler, 4", 9 oz........	5.00
Plate, 6" Sherbet	2.50		

ROYAL LACE
(pink, green, crystal, blue)
HAZEL ATLAS GLASS COMPANY 1934-1941

	Pink/Blue
Bowl, 4¾" Cream Soup ..	9.00/17.00
Bowl, 5" Berry	9.00/15.00
Bowl, 10" Round Berry ...	10.00/25.00
Bowl, 10", 3 Leg, Straight Edge	13.50/28.00
Bowl, 10", 3 Leg, Rolled Edge	14.00/55.00
Bowl, 10", 3 Leg, Ruffled Edge	15.00/35.00
Bowl, 11" Oval Vegetable	12.00/22.50
Butter Dish and Cover ...	85.00/265.00
Candlesticks, Pr., Straight Edge	20.00/55.00
Candlesticks, Pr., Rolled Edge	25.00/65.00

	Pink/Blue
Candlestick, Pr., Ruffled Edge	27.50/60.00
Cookie Jar and Cover ...	27.50/145.00
Creamer, Footed	7.00/17.50
Cup	5.25/15.50
Pitcher, 54 oz., Staight Sides	32.50/60.00
Pitcher, 8", 68 oz.	32.50/80.00
Pitcher, 8", 86 oz.	50.00/95.00
Pitcher, 8½" , 96 oz.	55.00/125.00
Plate, 6" Sherbet	2.75/6.00
Plate, 8½" Luncheon	5.50/15.00
Plate, 10" Dinner	7.00/21.50
Plate, 9-7/8" Grill.......	8.00/16.00
Platter, 13" Oval........	15.00/26.00
Salt and Pepper, Pr......	32.50/140.00

	Pink/Blue		Pink/Blue
Saucer	3.50/5.00	Tumbler, 3½", 5 oz.	12.00/22.00
Sherbet, Footed	7.00/17.50	Tumbler, 4-1/8", 9 oz.	9.00/18.00
Sugar	6.00/15.00	Tumbler, 4-7/8", 12 oz.	12.00/25.00
Sugar Lid	10.00/40.00	Tumbler, 5-3/8", 13 oz.	14.00/29.00

ROYAL RUBY (red)
ANCHOR HOCKING GLASS COMPANY 1939-1960's

	Red		Red
Ash Tray, 4½" Square . . .	2.50	Punch Cup	2.50
Bowl, 4¼" Berry	3.00	Saucer (Round or Square)	1.50
Bowl, 7½" Soup	7.50	Sherbet, Footed	4.50
Bowl, 8" Oval		Sugar, Flat	4.50
Vegetable	8.50	Sugar, Footed	5.50
Bowl, 8½" Large Berry . .	8.00	Tumbler, 3½ oz. Cocktail	5.50
Creamer, Flat	4.50	Tumbler, 5 oz., Juice,	
Creamer, Footed	5.50	2 Styles	4.00
Cup (Round or Square) . .	3.00	Tumbler, 9 oz. Water	4.00
Goblet, Ball Stem	8.50	Tumbler, 10 oz. Water . . .	4.50
Lamp	17.50	Tumbler, 13 oz. Iced Tea .	6.50
Pitcher, 42 oz., Tilted		Tumbler, 2½ oz. Footed	
or Upright	15.00	Wine	7.00
Pitcher, 3 qt., Tilted		Vase, 4" Ball Shaped	3.50
or Upright	20.00	Vase, 6½" Bulbous, Tall .	7.50
Plate, 6½" Sherbet	1.50	Vases, Several Styles	
Plate, 7" Salad	3.00	(Small)	5.00
Plate, 7¾" Luncheon	3.25	Vases, Several Styles	
Plate, 9" or 9¼" Dinner . .	5.00	(Large)	8.50
Punch Bowl and Stand . . .	30.00		

"S" PATTERN, "STIPPLED ROSE BAND"
(crystal, amber)
MACBETH EVANS GLASS COMPANY 1930-1933

	Crystal/Amber		Crystal/Amber
Bowl, 5½" Cereal	2.00/3.00	Plate, 13" Heavy Cake	30.00/50.00
Bowl, 8½" Large Berry	6.00/12.00	Saucer	1.25/1.50
Creamer, Thick or Thin	3.00/4.00	Sherbet, Low Footed	3.00/4.50
Cup, Thick or Thin	2.00/3.00	Sugar, Thick and Thin	3.00/4.00
Pitcher, 80 oz.	30.00/65.00	Tumbler, 3½", 5 oz.	2.50/4.50
Plate, 6" Sherbet	1.25/1.50	Tumbler, 4", 9 oz.	
Plate, 8" Luncheon	2.00/2.50	(Green: 30.00)	3.00/5.00
Plate, 9¼" Dinner	2.50/4.00	Tumbler, 4¼", 10 oz.	3.50/5.50
Plate, Grill	2.50/4.00	Tumbler, 5", 12 oz.	4.50/6.00
Plate, 11" Heavy Cake	25.00/-----		

SANDWICH (See Reproduction Section Page 153)
crystal, 1930-1960's - amber (desert gold), 1960's - pink & ruby red, 1939-1940 - forest green, 1950's-1960's - white (opaque), 1950's
HOCKING GLASS COMPANY 1939-1964

	Crystal/Green
Bowl, 4-7/8" Berry	2.00/1.50
Bowl, 6" Cereal	9.00/-----
Bowl, 6½" Smooth or Scalloped	2.50/15.00
Bowl, 7" Salad	3.50/20.00
Bowl, 8" Smooth or Scalloped	4.00/25.00
Bowl, 8¼" Oval	3.50/-----
Butter Dish, Low	25.00/-----
Cookie Jar and Cover	22.50/-----
Creamer	3.00/12.50
Cup, Tea or Coffee	1.50/11.00
Custard Cup	2.50/1.50
Custard Cup Liner	5.00/1.25

	Crystal/Green
Pitcher, 6" Juice	32.50/65.00
Pitcher, ½ gal., Ice Lip	37.50/150.00
Plate, 7" Dessert	4.00/1.00
Plate, 9" Dinner	7.00/29.00
Plate, 9" Indent For Punch Cup	2.50/-----
Plate, 12" Sandwich	6.00/-----
Saucer	1.25/2.00
Sherbet, Footed	3.50/-----
Sugar and Cover	7.50/12.50
Tumbler, 5 oz. Juice	4.00/2.00
Tumbler, 9 oz. Water	4.00/2.50
Tumbler, 9 oz. Footed	9.00/-----

SANDWICH (See Reproduction Section Page 154)
(crystal, amber, pink, red, teal blue, light green)
INDIANA GLASS COMPANY 1920-1970's

	Crystal/Pink
Ash Tray Set (Club, Spade, Heart, Diamond Shapes) each	2.00/-----
Bowl, 4¼" Berry	2.25/3.00
Bowl, 6"	3.00/3.50
Bowl, 6", 6 Sides	3.00/3.50
Bowl, 8¼"	7.00/10.00
Bowl, 9" Console	10.00/15.00
Bowl, 10" Console	12.00/18.00
Butter Dish and Cover Domed	65.00/150.00
Candlesticks, 3½", Pr.	8.00/13.00
Candlesticks, 7", Pr.	20.00/35.00
Creamer	4.00/6.00
Cruet, 6½" oz. and Stopper	37.50/-----
Cup	2.00/4.00
Creamer and Sugar on Diamond Shaped Tray	12.00/-----
Decanter and Stopper	35.00/65.00
Goblet, 9 oz.	9.00/12.00

	Crystal/Pink
Pitcher, 68 oz.	45.00/75.00
Plate, 6" Sherbet	1.25/2.50
Plate, 7" Bread and Butter	1.50/3.00
Plate, 8" Oval, Indent for Sherbet	2.50/3.50
Plate, 8-3/8" Luncheon	2.50/4.00
Plate, 10½" Dinner	8.00/12.00
Plate, 13" Sandwich	6.00/10.00
Sandwich Server, Center Handle	17.50/25.00
Saucer	1.50/2.00
Sugar	4.00/6.00
Tumbler, 3 oz. Footed Cocktail	15.00/-----
Tumbler, 8 oz. Footed Water	10.00/-----
Tumbler, 12 oz. Footed Iced Tea	12.00/-----
Wine 3", 4 oz.	7.00/-----

SHARON, "CABBAGE ROSE"
(See Reproduction Section, Page 155)
(pink, green, amber, crystal)
FEDERAL GLASS COMPANY 1935-1939

	Amber/Pink
Bowl, 5" Berry	4.50/5.50
Bowl, 5" Cream Soup	15.00/22.50
Bowl, 6" Cereal	8.00/11.50
Bowl, 7½", Flat Soup Two Inches Deep	20.00/20.00
Bowl, 8½" Large Berry	3.25/7.50
Bowl, 9½" Oval Vegetable	7.00/10.50
Bowl, 10½" Fruit	10.00/12.50
Butter Dish and Cover	32.50/37.50
Cake Plate, Footed, 11½"	14.00/17.00
Candy Jar and Cover	24.00/27.50
Cheese Dish and Cover	-----/450.00
Creamer, Footed	5.00/7.50
Cup	6.50/8.00
Jam Dish, 7½"	24.00/60.00
Pitcher, 80 oz., With or	

	Amber/Pink
Without Ice Lip	72.50/80.00
Plate, 6" Bread and Butter	2.00/3.25
Plate, 7½" Salad	7.00/12.00
Plate, 9½" Dinner	7.00/8.50
Platter, 12½" Oval	7.50/10.00
Salt and Pepper, Pr.	27.50/35.00
Saucer	2.00/3.50
Sherbet, Footed	6.50/7.50
Sugar	5.00/6.50
Sugar Lid	12.50/15.00
Tumbler, 4-1/8", 9 oz. Thick or Thin	15.00/17.00
Tumbler, 5¼", 12 oz. Thick or Thin	21.00/25.00
Tumbler, 6½", Footed, 15 oz.	37.50/27.50

SIERRA, "PINWHEEL"
(pink, green)
JEANNETTE GLASS COMPANY 1931-1933

	Pink/Green		Pink/Green
Bowl, 5½" Cereal	4.50/5.00	Platter, 11" Oval	10.00/12.00
Bowl, 8½" Large Berry	8.00/10.00	Salt and Pepper, Pr.	20.00/25.00
Bowl, 9½" Oval		Saucer	2.50/2.50
Vegetable	12.00/15.00	Serving Tray, 2 Handles	6.00/7.00
Butter Dish and Cover	38.00/41.00	Sugar	4.00/4.50
Creamer	7.50/7.50	Sugar Cover	8.00/9.00
Cup	5.00/7.50	Tumbler, 4½", 9 oz.	
Pitcher, 6½", 32 oz.	30.00/55.00	Footed	15.00/22.50
Plate, 9" Dinner	4.50/7.00		

SPIRAL
(green)
HOCKING GLASS COMPANY 1928-1930

	Green		Green
Bowl, 4¾" Berry	4.00	Preserve and Cover	15.00
Bowl, 7" Mixing	4.00	Salt and Pepper, Pr.	15.50
Bowl, 8" Large Berry	6.00	Sandwich Server, Center	
Creamer, Flat or Footed .	4.00	Handle	12.50
Cup	3.00	Saucer	1.00
Ice or Butter Tub	12.00	Sherbet	2.50
Pitcher, 7-5/8", 58 oz. . . .	15.00	Sugar, Flat or Footed	4.00
Plate, 6" Sherbet	1.00	Tumbler, 3", 5 oz. Juice . .	2.50
Plate, 8" Luncheon	2.00	Tumbler, 5", 9 oz. Water .	3.50

STARLIGHT
(pink, white, crystal)
HAZEL ATLAS GLASS COMPANY 1938-1940

	Crystal/Pink
Bowl, 5½" Cereal.......	2.00/3.00
Bowl, 8½", Closed Handles.............	3.00/8.00
Bowl, 11½" Salad.......	10.00/15.00
Plate, 6" Bread and Butter..............	2.00/2.50
Creamer, Oval	3.00/-----
Cup..................	2.50/2.50

	Crystal/Pink
Plate, 8½" Luncheon	2.00/3.00
Plate, 9" Dinner	3.00/5.00
Plate, 13" Sandwich	4.00/7.00
Relish Dish.............	2.50/4.50
Salt and Pepper, Pr......	12.50/-----
Saucer	1.00/2.00
Sugar, Oval	3.00/-----

STRAWBERRY
(pink, green, iridescent)
U. S. GLASS COMPANY 1928-1931

	Pink or Green		Pink or Green
Bowl, 4" Berry	5.00	Pickle Dish	8.00
Bowl, 6½" Deep Salad . .	8.00	Pitcher, 7¾"	100.00
Bowl, 7½" Deep Berry . . .	10.00	Plate, 6" Sherbet	4.75
Butter Dish and Cover . . .	100.00	Plate, 7½" Salad	7.00
Compote, 5¾"	10.00	Sherbet	5.50
Creamer, Small	8.00	Sugar, Small, Open	10.00
Creamer, Large, 4-5/8" . .	12.00	Sugar Large	10.00
Olive Dish, 5", One		Sugar Cover	15.00
Handled	7.50	Tumbler, 3-5/8", 9 oz. . . .	17.50

SUNFLOWER
(pink, green)
JEANNETTE GLASS COMPANY Late 1920's

	Pink or Green		Pink or Green
Ash Tray, 5", Center Design Only	6.00	Saucer	2.00
Cake Plate, 10", 3 Legs	5.00	Sugar	6.50
Creamer	6.50	Tumbler, 4¾", 8 oz. Footed	10.50
Cup	5.25	Trivet, 7", 3 Legs, Turned Up Edge	90.00
Plate, 9" Dinner	6.25		

SWIRL, "PETAL SWIRL"
(pink, ultra-marine, delphite)
JEANNETTE GLASS COMPANY 1937-1938

	Pink/Ultra-marine		Pink/Ultra marine
Bowl, 5¼" Cereal	4.00/6.00	Plate, 7¼"	3.50/5.00
Bowl, 9" Salad	8.00/11.00	Plate, 8" Salad	4.00/8.00
Bowl, 10" Footed, Closed Handles	-----/17.50	Plate, 9¼" Dinner	4.50/6.50
Bowl, 10½" Console, Footed	10.00/12.00	Plate, 12½" Sandwich	6.00/9.00
		Salt and Pepper, Pr.	-----/20.00
Butter Dish	125.00/185.00	Saucer	1.50/2.00
Candleholders, Double Branch, Pr.	-----/17.50	Sherbet, Low Footed	4.25/7.00
		Soup - Tab Handles (Lug)	12.00/12.50
Candy Dish, Open, 3 Legs	4.00/5.00	Sugar, Footed	4.50/5.50
Candy Dish with Cover	45.00/60.00	Tumbler, 4", 9 oz.	6.50/9.50
Coaster, 1" x 3¼"	5.00/6.00	Tumbler, 4¾", 12 oz.	12.00/22.50
Creamer, Footed	5.00/6.50	Tumbler, 9 oz., Footed	10.00/15.00
Cup	3.00/4.50	Vase, 6½", Footed	9.50/12.00
Plate, 6½" Sherbet	1.50/2.50	Vase, 8½", Footed	-----/14.00

136

TEA ROOM
(green, pink)
INDIANA GLASS COMPANY 1926-1931

	Pink or Green		Pink or Green
Bowl, 7½" Banana Split .	8.50	Plate, 10½", Two	
Bowl, 8½" Celery	10.00	Handled	18.00
Bowl, 8¾" Deep Salad . .	30.00	Relish, Divided	7.50
Bowl, 9½" Oval		Salt and Pepper, Pr.	30.00
Vegetable	32.50	Saucer	9.00
Candlestick, Low, Pr.	25.00	Sherbet, Three Styles . . .	10.00
Creamer, 4"	10.00	Sugar, 4"	10.00
Creamer and Sugar on		Sugar, Flat with Cover . . .	20.00
Tray, 3½"	30.00	Sundae, Footed	10.00
Cup	12.50	Tumbler, 8½ oz.	15.00
Goblet, 9 oz.	15.00	Tumbler, 6 oz., Footed . .	11.00
Ice Bucket	27.50	Tumbler, 9 oz., Footed . .	10.50
Lamp, 9" Electric	27.50	Tumbler, 11 oz., Footed .	13.00
Mustard, Covered	42.50	Tumbler, 12 oz., Footed .	20.00
Parfait	9.00	Vase, 9"	22.50
Pitcher, 64 oz.	75.00	Vase, 11" Ruffled Edge	
Plate, 6½" Sherbet	6.50	or Straight	22.00
Plate, 8¼" Luncheon	16.50		

THISTLE
(pink, green)
MACBETH-EVANS 1929-1930

	Pink/Green		Pink/Green
Bowl, 5½" Cereal	9.00/12.50	Plate, 10¼" Grill	10.00/10.00
Bowl, 10¼" Large Fruit . .	125.00/75.00	Plate, 13" Heavy Cake . . .	60.00/55.00
Cup, Thin	3.00/12.00	Saucer	6.00/6.00
Plate, 8" Luncheon	7.00/9.00		

TWISTED OPTIC
(pink, green, amber, crystal)
IMPERIAL GLASS COMPANY 1927-1930

	Pink or Green		Pink or Green
Bowl, 4¾" Cream Soup . .	5.00	Preserve (Same as Candy	
Bowl, 5" Cereal	1.75	but with Slot in lid)	15.00
Bowl, 7" Salad or Soup . .	5.00	Sandwich Server, Center	
Candlesticks, 3", Pr.	8.50	Handle	9.50
Candy Jar and Cover	12.50	Sandwich Server,	
Creamer	4.50	Two Handled Flat	5.50
Cup	2.50	Saucer	1.00
Pitcher, 64 oz.	15.00	Sherbet	4.00
Plate, 6" Sherbet	1.50	Sugar	4.50
Plate, 7" Salad	1.75	Tumbler, 4½", 9 oz.	4.00
Plate, 8" Luncheon	2.00	Tumbler, 5¼", 12 oz.	6.00

"VICTORY"
(amber, green, pink, cobalt blue)
DIAMOND GLASS-WARE COMPANY 1929-1932

	All Colors		All Colors
Bowl, 6½" Cereal.......	5.00	Mayonnaise Set: 3½"	
Bowl, 8½" Flat Soup	8.00	Tall, 5½" Across, 8½"	
Bowl, 12" Console	12.00	Indented Plate w/Ladle	20.00
Candlesticks, 3", Pr.	12.50	Plate, 6" Bread and	
Compote, 6" Tall,		Butter..............	2.00
6¾" Diameter........	6.25	Plate, 7" Salad	2.50
Creamer	4.50	Plate, 8" Luncheon	3.00
Cup..................	3.00	Plate, 9" Dinner	5.00
Goblet, 5", 7 oz.	10.00	Sandwich Server, Center	
Gravy Boat and Platter ..	75.00	Handle	12.50
		Saucer	1.50
		Sugar	4.50

VITROCK ("FLOWER RIM")
(white)
ANCHOR HOCKING GLASS COMPANY 1934-late 1930's

	White		White
Bowl, Cream Soup, 5½" .	2.50	Plate, Luncheon, 8¾" ...	1.75
Bowl, Fruit, 6"	2.50	Plate, Soup, 9"	2.00
Bowl, Cereal, 7½"	2.50	Plate, Dinner, 10"	2.50
Bowl, Vegetable	4.00	Platter, 11½"	4.00
Creamer, Oval	2.50	Saucer	.75
Cup	1.50	Sugar, Oval	2.50
Plate, Salad, 7¼"	1.00		

WATERFORD, "WAFFLE"
(crystal, pink)
HOCKING GLASS COMPANY 1938-1944

	Crystal/Pink
Ash Tray, 4"	2.50/5.00
Bowl, 4¾" Berry	3.50/4.50
Bowl, 5½" Cereal	6.00/9.00
Bowl, 8¼" Large Berry ..	5.50/8.00
Butter Dish and Cover ...	12.50/165.00
Coaster, 4"	1.50/3.00
Creamer, Oval	2.50/7.00
Cup	3.25/9.00
Goblet, 5¼", 5-5/8"	8.50/-----
Pitcher, 42 oz., Juice, Tilted	14.00/-----
Pitcher, 80 oz., Ice Lip, Tilted	22.50/95.00
Plate, 6" Sherbet	1.75/3.00

	Crystal/Pink
Plate, 7-1/8" Salad	2.00/3.00
Plate, 9-5/8" Dinner	4.00/7.50
Plate, 10¼", Handled Cake	4.00/8.00
Plate, 13¾" Sandwich ...	4.25/6.00
Salt and Pepper, 2 Types .	5.00/-----
Saucer	1.00/2.00
Sherbet, Footed	2.50/6.00
Sugar	1.25/3.00
Sugar Cover, Oval	2.50/7.00
Tumbler, 4-7/8", 10 oz. Footed	6.00/8.50
Vase, 6¾"	8.00/-----

WINDSOR, "WINDSOR DIAMOND"
(pink, green, crystal)
JEANNETTE GLASS COMPANY 1932-1946

	Crystal/Pink		Crystal/Pink
Ash Tray, 5¾"	10.00/25.00	Pitcher, 6¾", 52 oz.	10.00/15.00
Bowl, 4¾" Berry	1.50/3.00	Plate, 6" Sherbet	1.25/2.25
Bowl, 5" Cream Soup	4.00/9.00	Plate, 7" Salad	2.50/6.50
Bowl, 5-1/8", 5-3/8"		Plate, 9" Dinner	2.00/5.00
Cereals	3.00/8.00	Plate, 10¼" Sandwich,	
Bowl, 7-1/8", Three Legs .	3.50/12.00	Handled	3.00/6.00
Bowl, 8½", Large Berry . .	4.00/7.00	Plate, 13-5/8" Chop	7.00/10.00
Bowl, 9½" Oval		Platter, 11½" Oval	2.50/6.00
Vegetable	4.50/8.00	Relish Platter, 11½"	
Bowl, 12½" Fruit Console	8.00/25.00	Divided	4.00/7.00
Bowl, 7"x11¾", Boat		Salt and Pepper, Pr.	10.00/20.00
Shape	10.00/15.00	Saucer	1.50/2.00
Butter Dish	20.00/27.50	Sherbet, Footed	2.00/4.50
Cake Plate, 13½" Thick . .	5.00/8.00	Sugar and Cover	4.00/9.00
Candlesticks, 3", Pr.	10.00/15.00	Tray, 4" Square	2.00/2.50
Candy Jar and Cover	7.00/15.00	Tray, 4-1/8"x9"	3.00/5.00
Coaster, 3¼"	2.00/3.00	Tray, 8½"x9¾"	6.00/15.00
Compote, ...	3.00/5.00	Tumbler, 3¼", 5 oz.	3.00/8.00
Creamer	2.50/5.00	Tumbler, 4", 9 oz.	4.00/7.00
Cup	2.00/4.50	Tumbler, 5", 12 oz.	5.00/10.00
Pitcher, 4½", 16 oz.	12.00/40.00		

REPRODUCTIONS

As popularity of any item in the collecting field grows, there is always someone or some company that will take advantage of the collector. This section will show you the reproductions in Depression Glass through May 1980.

Know your glassware or your dealer before spending your hard earned cash for it; also, be wary of deals that seem too good to be true.

The items pictured in this section have all been reproduced since 1973 either by the original glass companies themselves or by private individuals.

Items introduced by companies are usually available in the local dish barns or merchant stores. Those privately manufactured are found at flea markets or local antique or junk shops.

Some of the glass is marketed through private sales or parties much like the "Tupperware" parties. In these, the buyer is treated to "exclusive lines" of glassware.

My personal feeling is that as long as people buy these reproductions, re-issues, new products made to look old, or what have you, then they will continue to be made either privately or by the companies themselves. I feel also that buying a collectible is an investment; but buying a reproduction is merely speculation. These latter products appeal to me as much as swamp land in Florida.

What can we do? First, we can educate ourselves to know glass; secondly, we can refrain from buying the newer glass. Barring that, we who know the reproductions can label them as such when the opportunity arises.

MAYFAIR (pink, green, blue)
Privately Produced 1977 . . .

Only the shot glass (which is rare in the original) has been made in this pattern. The green (totally wrong color) and blue are no problem since the shot glasses have never been found in these colors originally. The difficulty comes with the pink.

Generally speaking, the newer shot glass has a heavier over-all look. The bottom area tends to have a thicker rim of glass. Often, the "pink" coloring isn't right; it may be too light, it may be too orange. However, if these cursory examinations fail, there are other points to check.

First, notice the stem of the flower. You have a single stem in the new flower. At the base of the stem in the old glass, the stem separates into an "A" shape. Further, look at the leaves on the stem. In the new design, the leaf itself is hollow with the veins molded in. In the old glass, the leaf portion is molded in and the veining is left hollow. In the center of the flower, the dots (anther) cluster entirely to one side of the old design and are rather distinct. Nothing like that occurs in the newer version.

AVOCADO
(pink, frosted pink, yellow, blue, red amethyst)
INDIANA GLASS Co. Tiara Exclusives Line, 1974 . . .

Thus far, the company has only overlapped the original glass colors in pink and only the pitcher and tumbler sets have been made. The original pink color is lighter in shade than this newer, slightly orange tint, pink.

Some of these sets, such as red, were made in limited editions as a selling point with buyers who are hopeful that someday they may be more valuable. Perhaps they shall; but I personally feel it will take many years for these to have more than their original value.

CHERRY BLOSSOM
(pink, green, blue, delphite)
Privately Produced 1973 . . .

    In 1973 the Depression Glass world was stunned with the appearance of a child's butter dish and some odd looking child's cups—odd because no child's butter dish was made originally and because in the bottoms of the cups, the cherry design was hanging upside down. Since then, the upside down design has been rectified and some saucers and plates have appeared. However, all these pieces haven't the sveltness of the original pieces and are easily spotted.

    In 1977 butter dishes and shakers appeared. Some shakers in pink and green were dated '77; other pink, green and delphite shakers appeared non dated. These shakers are readily recognizable by the almost squared protrusions around the top edge of the shakers. I call them helicopter blades. On the original shakers these protrusions are more rounded and they extend only slightly outward from the top. If you wish to carry your examinations further than that, the design on the shakers is weaker in spots on the newer versions.

The butter dishes pose a bit more problem in disinguishing old from new except in the pretty blue color which wasn't an original color. However, if you use your tactile sense and feel the design inside the butter top, you will find it very sharply defined in the new; also, the knob on the new top is very sharply defined whereas in the old, the knob is more smoothly formed.

Again, about ½" from the edge of the new top, you will notice one band. In the old, there are two distinct bands to be noted here.

The pitcher and tumblers appeared in August 1979. The easiest method to determine the new is to look at the bottom. The pattern is weakly struck and there appears to be pieces of straw among the leaves and cherries on the pitcher bottom.

The veins in the leaves are raised and the leaves are hollow on the new; whereas, the old pieces have the veins hollow and the leaves raised.

IRIS
(crystal and sprayed on mixed colors such as yellow/green; yellow/red)
Jeanette Glass Company 1977 . . .

Produced by the original company, the candy bottom and vase have been made in multi-colors as well as crystal and irridescent. Notice that the bottom of the new candy pictured is plain whereas all the originals are rayed. This is true of both candy bottoms and vases. The newer colors are easily spotted, of course; but notice the bottom when buying crystal or iridized.

MADRID
(amber)
Federal Glass Co. 1976-1977

Introduced by Federal as "Recollection" in 1976 ostensibly for the Bi-Centennial each piece is dated '76 as shown here on a plate edge. The color is a deeper amber than the old.

For price comparison, here is what the new sold for in stores.

Plate, 11" dinner	4 for $6.00
Plate, 8¼" salad	4 for $4.58
Cup	4 for $3.50
Saucer	4 for $3.50
Bowl, 7½" soup	4 for $4.50

Bowl, 9½" square	$6.00
Bowl, oval vegetable	$6.00
Butter dish and cover	$6.00
20 piece starter set	
(4 dinners, 4 salads, 4 cups,	
4 saucers, 4 soups)	$19.00

The butter dish knob has mold marks running from north to south on the new; the mold marks run east to west on the old. I mention this only because on occasion new tops are "married" to old bottoms in an attempt to do a bit of "wool pulling". In my area, the starter sets are now down to $9.95 and still not selling whereas the butter dish is sold out.

Other items introduced in 1977 are candleholders, creamer and sugar with no lid, a footed candy and cover, a footed square bowl, and a footed cake plate. These last three footed pieces are not duplicates of the original Madrid. However, due to the first issues not selling so well, many stores failed to stock these latter pieces.

Many collectors bought these sets up when the Federal Glass Company went out of business, but since these will never be used, it is doubtful that they are a good investment since so many were made.

MISS AMERICA
(crystal, green, pink, ice blue, red amberina)
Privately Produced 1977 . . .

The butter dish in this pattern is probably the best of the newer products. There seems to be three major differences between the original and the new butter top; and since the value of the butter dish lies in the top, it seems more profitable to examine it.

Notice the red butter dish pictured for an example of the first difference. See the curved, skirt-like edge to each panel? In the original dish, the panels come straight down. There is no curving at the edge of the panel.

Second, pick up the top and feel up inside it. If the butter top knob is filled with glass so that it is convex (curved outward), it is new; the old inside knob area is concave (curved inward).

Finally, from the underside, look through the top at the knob. In the original butter dish you should see a perfectly formed multi-sided star; in the newer version all you will see are distorted rays of the star with no points visible.

Shakers have been made in green, pink and crystal also.

152

SANDWICH
(crystal)
Anchor Hocking Glass Co.

At present, only the cookie jar has been re-introduced to use the jargon of day. However, we may assume that if sales are good for this item, we will see others. The newer jar is much larger when compared with the old.

	New	Old
Height	10¼"	9¼"
Opening Width	5½"	4 7/8"
Diameter/Largest Part	22"	19"

SANDWICH
(amber, blue, red, crystal)
Indiana Glass Co. Tiara Exclusive Line 1969 . . .

   In recent years Sandwich in amber, the smokey blue shown here and a sprayed red over crystal have been issued. In 1969 came red in quite a few pieces and these are difficult to tell from the older pieces of the 1930's. Any piece you see in amber or blue is of recent origin.
   Bad news for collectors came in 1978 when Tiara announced that they were going to issue the Sandwich in crystal from decanter sets down to the domed butter dish. My advice here is to be wary of paying any high prices for the old at this time. Since the original molds are being used, there is little difference.

SHARON
(blue, dark green, light green, pink, burnt umber)
Privately Produced 1976 . . .

A blue Sharon butter turned up in 1976 and created a sensation. The blue was the color of Mayfair blue; but this color was unknown in Sharon pattern. This fluke helped to quickly inform Depression enthusiasts that new editions were being made available.

In similar colors, you can distinguish between the old and the new butter dishes by noticing that the bottom ridge of the newer butter dish is sharply defined; the old bottom ledge is barely defined. Also, the top of the newer butter dish is heavier and thicker than the old—in most instances, it even weighs more. The knob is easier to grasp on the new butter dishes as it sticks up higher and you've more room to fit your finger around the knob and grasp the top. In the old butter dish tops, the knob fits so closely to the top that it makes it hard to grasp the knob.

In 1977 a "cheese dish" appeared having the same top as the butter. I put the name in quotes because it is but a parody of the original cheese dish. The new bottom of the dish is about half way between a flat plate and a butter dish bottom and is over thick giving it an awkward appearance. The real cheese dish bottom more nearly resembles a salad plate with a raised rim. These "cheese dishes" are easily spotted as being new.

GLOSSARY OF TERMS

Amber—brownish yellow color (see Madrid or Patrician picture for example).

Amethyst—a light, pastel purple as opposed to black amethyst which appears black until held to strong light whereby it shows deep purple.

Apricot—a dark yellow color, yet lighter in shade than amber; usually used to describe the darker shade of Princess than topaz.

A O P—abbreviation for "all over pattern" usually used to describe Cherry Blossom.

Berry Bowl—term used by many glass companies to describe a round bowl.

BonBon—a candy dish, usually uncovered.

Bread & Butter Plate—usually a six inch plate in a pattern that does not have a sherbet.

Cake Plate—a heavy, flat plate, usually having 3 legs.

Carnival—older, iridized glassware from eary 1900's; also term used to describe the color of Floragold or an iridized pattern.

Celery—usually a long, narrow, flat dish; in Colonial, a two handled dish taller than the sugar.

Cheese Dish—a covered dish, the bottom of which is normally flatter than that of the butter dish.

Chigger Bite—a term auctioneers use to describe a small chip on a dish.

Chop Plate—a large, flat plate called a salver by some companies.

Chunked—a polite way to describe a badly damaged piece of glass.

Claret—a goblet of varying size depending upon company terminology.

Closed Handled—having solid tab handles.

Coaster—glass liner sometimes doubling as an ash tray.

Cobalt Blue—a deep, dark blue color (shown in Moderntone or Moondrops).

Comport/Compote—term used to denote small, open candy dish which is stemmed.

Concentric Rings—circles within circles; gradually increasing or decreasing sized circles.

Console Bowl—centerpiece bowl, usually with candlesticks.

Cordial—goblet of varying size depending upon company terminology.

Cracker Jar—term for what would be a modern day cookie jar; they were sold with certain brands of products packed inside them.

Cream Soup—a two handled bouillon or consomme dish.

Decanter—usually a stoppered bottle for wine.

Delphite—a light blue opaque color; sometimes referred to as "blue milk glass".

Demitasse—a smaller than normal cup with saucer.

Domino Tray—a tray with a ring for creamer to reside in; the remaining surface within the tray being meant to hold sugar cubes.

Ebony—black color.

Etched—design cut into glass; usually found on better quality glass.

Fired-On—color applied and baked on at the factory.

Flashed-On—color added over crystal; usually wears off as opposed to the fired-on color which does not wear off with use.

Flat—a non footed dish; dish without a footed base or stem.

Fluted—scalloped edged.

Frog—heavy glass holed flower stem holder.

Goblet—a stemmed, bowl shaped tumbler.

Gravy Boat—oval shaped bowl used for serving gravy; often with a type of spout.

Grill Plate—a usually tri-sectioned plate of the type used in restaurants to keep the meat and vegetables divided from each other.

Hat Shaped—bowl looking like an up-turned hat.

Hot Plate—glass plate used for setting hot items on the table as a protection for the table or table spread.

Ice Blue—very light, crystal blue color.

Ice Bucket—a milk bucket like container for holding ice cubes.

Ice Lip—a guard or fold moulded about the lip of a pitcher to keep ice from falling out into the glass when pouring from the pitcher.

Jadite—an opaque, light green color.

Jam Jar—small, covered jar for holding jam or preserves.

Luncheon Plate—usually an 8-9 inch plate, smaller than a dinner plate.

Mayonnaise—an open, cone shaped compote.

Milk Glass—a white glassware, the color of milk, usually heavy.

Mold/Mould—a usually two part encasement into which hot glass is poured and a glass object is formed; depression glass was primarily a glassware made from molds rather than being blown or formed by hand.

Monax—white color produced by Macbeth Evans, usually very thin.

Motif—the pattern or design on glass.

Mug—a heavy cup, usually flat bottomed.

Nappy—old word denoting a bowl.

Opalescent—white rimmed flowing into color.

Open Handled—handles having an opening for the finger or hand to reach through.

Parfait—a tall, ice cream dish of the type used for sundaes in soda fountains of by-gone days.

Pickle Dish—an oblong dish used for serving pickles; smaller than a celery.

157

Platinum Band—an applied silver colored rim on glassware.

Platonite—Hazel Atlas heat resistant white glass often colored by a fired-on process.

Platter—oblong or oval shaped meat dish.

Preserve Dish—tall, footed dish often used as a candy.

Rayed—arrows or spoke-like designs on glass bottoms.

Relish—oblong dish, sometimes referred to as a pickle dish.

Rolled Edge—glassware having an edge curved in toward or out away from center.

Rope Edge—glassware with an edge having a rope-like design embedded in it.

Rose Bowl—small, curved in edged bowl, usually having a small center hole and usually tri-footed.

Salad Plate—usually 7-7½ inch plate, for serving salads.

Salver—large, 11-12 inch, non handled serving plate.

Sandwich Server—a salver or sometimes a handled, often center handled, serving plate.

S A S E—short for self addressed, stamped envelope.

Sherbet—small, usually footed, ice cream or dessert dish.

Teal—a blue-green color in all companies except Jeannette.

Tid-Bit—a two or three tiered serving dish made of increasingly smaller plates connected by a center metal pole, around 12-15 inches tall.

Topaz—bright yellow colored glassware.

Trivet—a three footed hot plate, usually about 7 inches in diameter; similar in design to three footed cake plates but much smaller in diameter.

Tumbler—a glass.

Tumble Up—a glass bottle with long neck having a small tumbler seated up-side down over the bottle neck serving as the bottle top; usually used on night stand by bed to quinch night time thirst.

Ultra-Marine—Jeannette's blue-green color.

Vaseline—a glowing yellow colored glassware similar to the color of the jelly-like substance of the same name.

Two Publications I recommend are:
Depression Glass Daze
THE ORIGINAL
NATIONAL DEPRESSION GLASS NEWSPAPER

Depression Glass Daze, the Original, National monthly newspaper dedicated to the buying, selling & collecting of colored **glassware** of the 20's and 30's. We average 48 pages each month filled with **feature** articles by top notch columnists, readers "finds", club happenings, show news, a china corner, a current listing of new glass issues to beware of and a multitude of ads!! You can find it in the DAZE! Keep up with what's happening in the dee gee world with a subscription to the DAZE. Buy, sell or trade from the convenience of your easy chair.

Name _____ Street _____

City_____State_____Zip_____

    ☐ 1 year-$8.00 ☐ 2 years $15.00 ☐ Check enclosed ☐ Please bill me
    ☐ Master Charge ☐ Visa [Foreign subscribers - please add $1.00 per year]

Exp. date _____ Card No._____

Signature_____

Orders to D.G.D., Box 57GF, Otisville, Mich. 48463 - Please allow 30 days

A MAGAZINE FOR COLLECTORS & DEALERS OF GLASS
established 1971

—12 ISSUES PER YEAR—
64 pages per month!

$9.50 - one year $18.00 - two years $25.00 - three years

or try a trial subscription for $2.00 (3 issues)

* INFORMATIVE ARTICLES BY RESPECTED COLUMNISTS/AUTHORS * TRADEMARKS *
REPRODUCTION UPDATES * BOOK REVIEWS * LOTS OF ADS—EVEN A SEPARATE SECTION ON "NEW" GLASS * RESEARCH * NEW STORES * MORE! Devoted to keeping glass collectors informed *

Enclose payment and send to: GLASS REVIEW, P.O. Box 2315-F, Costa Mesa, CA 92626 or call (714)642-7636.

Additional Books By
Gene Florence

Collectors Encyclopedia of Depression Glass
$14.95

Collectors Encyclopedia of Occupied Japan
$12.95

Collectors Encyclopedia of Occupied Japan II
$12.95

Collectors Encyclopedia of Akro Agate
$8.95

Add $1.00 postage for the first book, $.35 for each additional book.

Copies of these books may be ordered from:

Gene Florence
P.O. Box 22186
Lexington, KY 40522
or
COLLECTOR BOOKS
P.O. Box 3009
Paducah, KY 42001